BOOK OF
AFRICAN
Spirituality

RA MERI

Conceptualised, researched, arranged,
written and edited by Ra Meri.
Published by Ra Meri Trust.

ISBN: 978-0-620-89288-9

MIA| Made In Africa

Contents

PREFACE

These stories are a form of advanced technology that was developed by African Sages. They are rich in symbolism and coded messaging. The **Book of African Spirituality** is an advanced form of storytelling.

When you read the stories, they imprint your mind with the wisdom that story represents. It is not just about knowing the story, although that is important too - but the symbols and verses invoke something wonderful deep within. They are actually alive. They are living wisdom passed down through many generations like a family heirloom.

They are not just imbued with meaning. They are impregnated with vitality and function. A function that arises from their wisdom.

The stories are a living heritage. A living body of truth. A living image of the **Hidden Intelligence** – known as **Neter**. They carry in them an advanced technology that when fully understood unlocks the true "Knowledge of Self" that African Sages such as Imhotep, were teaching.

Ra Meri
April 27, 2020
Made In Africa

BOOK OF AFRICAN SPIRITUALITY

Book of

Maat

Chapter 0

PRINCE SETNA

1. The Book that made Prince Setna such a great African sage, Maa Kheru, whose word is true, was the Book of Maat. This book was passed down from generation to generation of great African sages, to be used to teach Initiates and the people of the African Nations, including Kamit, Nehes, Nubia and Punt. The African sage, Prince Setna, was so great and loved that people sang songs about him, son of the Great Rameses, most learned man in Kamit.

2. He was a great scholar, he was able to read all of the old writings and decipher the most ancient of texts. No symbol in Kamit was unknown to him, even the ones on the walls of the crumbling temples from the oldest of days.

3. He was also a mighty magician, skilled in Hekau, perhaps the mightiest in Kamit, and in the world, for he had learned the magical arts from the secret texts that not even the Priests of the Nile, or any priests for that matter, could read.

4. Because of this, he would often spend his days studying the Book of Maat, and other ancient writings and listening to the stories told by the

elders and the scribes. Every day his servants would bring him rolls of papyrus from libraries and temples all over Kamit.

5. He would read the rolls of papyrus, including the Book of Maat, and his scribes would make copies of them to place in his father's library. Thus Rameses' kingdom was a wise kingdom of learning.

6. This is the Book of Maat which contains 42 Laws of Neter that Prince Setna read and memorised every day in the morning when he woke up, after eating, and at night before he slept. Every night before he slept, just like all the other Initiates in Kamit, Prince Setna would declare to himself, that he has not violated any of the Laws of Neter. Moreover, in the mornings Prince Setna would also repeat this Ritual of Weighing His Deeds and Words against the 42 Laws of Maat. If he found himself to have violated any of the 42 Laws he would note it down and vow to himself to be more conscious of his Deeds and Words, the following day, so as to live by Maat.

7. It was the goal of every African to live by Maat and be judged daily, as well as when you die, by your Ba to be Maa Kheru, True of Voice, or True of Word and Deed. Living by Maat was the Standard by which all men and women were measured in the community. This is fundamentally what kept the African Community and Nations intact, purposeful, true and whole. Anything not in accordance with Maat was seen as taboo, or Isfet, chaos, the fruits of Set, the wayward Ego. Set was a trickster Neter, known to have a forked-tongue and no respectful African wanted to fall

for his tricks and be associated with Set. "There is no substitute for African Culture, History, Traditions, and Spirituality" his father, Rameses, used to advise him. So he took the Book of Maat and the Rituals seriously and studiously.

8. Rameses also told his son that, "When Ausar became King of Kamit, the men and women that he came to rule were in a chaotic and unruly state. They were nomadic tribes in constant warfare against each other. They were given over to evil and chaotic behaviour. He brought spirituality to the people thus enabling them to achieve life, prosperity and wellness. He gave them a Book of Laws to regulate their conduct, settled their disputes justly, and instructed them in the science of spiritual development. The Book of Laws that Ausar taught the Kamityu is the Book of Maat. This is what our great-great-great grand Neter used to establish the Kingdom of Kamit."

9. The Nesu, Rameses, would also say to his young prince, "These 42 Laws of Neter are a National treasure, more precious than gold, and so precious that if a man or woman should know them, here on Earth and thereafter, it would propel him or her safely and soundly through the Duat, such that the Ammit would not devour his or her Ab, when the Ab is weighed against the Feather of Maat." No one knew who wrote the Book of Maat. But they knew that its source was the Neter Tehuti and that it was revealed by the Neter Maat. It was also well known that the people who codified it into Law, are the African Priests of the

Nile. Prince Setna recalls the words that Aankhu said to him regarding the book:

I HAVE NOT DONE INEQUITY

The ultimate goal of every African is embodied in this law, and it is considered the master law. It is a statement of culmination, encompassing all of the following 42 laws of Neter, or declarations. Through living a consciously lawful life, the Initiate hopes to one day make the statement that they have freed themselves of the "fetters of Set", iniquity. This is a statement of clear conscious.

Chapter 2

I HAVE NOT ROBBED WITH VIOLENCE

This is an interesting declaration for it puts a qualification on robbery which in and of itself is mostly considered an act of wrong. However, there are times when one may find themselves in a position that they had not foreseen for themselves. In certain situations you may find yourself in a position where you must commit what one may consider a "lesser evil" for the greater good, or your life and survival may be at stake. The people around you may not be friendly towards you and you may not have any money, it may be a time of chaos or revolution. Whatever the case may be, you should always strive towards the greater good.

Chapter 3

I HAVE NOT DONE VIOLENCE TO ANY MAN

This declaration is speaking to unwarranted violence. Unwarranted violence is an act of animalism. In fact, it is below animalism, for most animals have some reason, usually instinctual, that guides their actions. However, man is above animals, and is a Divine and rational being, and therefore she should use this faculty of reasoning and problem solving to find the best solution in every situation before resorting to committing acts of violence.

Chapter 4

I HAVE NOT COMMITTED THEFT

As stated in the preceding law, this is referring to "un-warranted" theft. Theft in general, like violence, is for the most part considered unwarranted. As a person, a man, you should attempt to exhaust all possibilities, and your faculties and capabilities before resorting to theft. Remember that All is an expression of Neter and that includes you, and what you do to another you do to Self, you do to Neter. We must think about the effect of our actions in the grand scheme of things. How will my taking of this sister's bread affect her? How will it affect her family? How will it affect my spiritual growth and development? Is this the only solution? One must think first and hard.

Chapter 5

I HAVE NOT SLAIN
NEITHER MAN
NOR WOMAN

Slaying a man or a woman is a grave act with major repercussions. The unwarranted murder of any person is a grave mistake, and places one in a position of major 'cause and effect' debt. Even in acts of Self-defence, murder should be the absolute last resort, and it should be something that one should try at all cost to avoid. Self-defence is the only bend in this law, and one should never be the aggressor.

Chapter 6

I HAVE NOT MADE LIGHT THE BUSHEL

One must not steal another person's property. Thou shalt not steal land or clothes or food or shelter or anything else, for that matter, that does not belong to them. There is a huge 'cause and effect' debt which is created on Earth when one steals. This debt will be paid eventually, and if not by you, then it is passed on to your bloodline.

Chapter 7

I HAVE NOT ACTED DECEITFULLY

In all things, our intentions should be pure, and we should do our best to make our intentions clear. Deceit is a serious offense, maybe even more serious than the preceding statements. One can find themselves stealing or killing through a response from their animal within, as an act of survival, but deceit requires intelligence. This is deceptive intelligence. In situations where we intentionally deceive another, we have taken the divine faculties of intelligence, and degraded them to evil use. In these situations we are the true embodiment of Set. Remember to kill Ausar, Set dealt deceitfully with him, making him think that he had good intentions. He said, "Ausar, here sen, try this nefer coffin." Then he shut the coffin and suffocated him. In these situations not only do we deceive and harm our brother or sister, but we intentionally use the Intelligence within for evil purposes. This is a great evil, that it takes time to redeem oneself from, for deceit says that one's conscience is weak, and they have not developed the will to ignore the sway of the animal within towards their intellect. If this is not cultivated in one's youth, then it will be a difficult uphill to climb.

Chapter 8

I HAVE NOT TAKEN THINGS WHICH BELONG TO NETER

It is clear that one must not steal offerings made to the Neteru in their shrines, or temples. It is someone's offering to the Creator and the Neteru, which is like a personal contract or agreement. One must never steal from the Neter Heru Behudet, as an example. In all truth you must understand that everything that exists, has a self-preservation mechanism, including the Neteru and it would be unwise to wrong a force of nature that is a part of you. It is the equivalent of plucking out your own eye. If you also consider the reality that there is only **One Being** in existence then there actually is no justification for stealing. Stealing from another is the same as stealing from yourself.

Chapter 9

I HAVE NOT UTTERED FALSEHOOD

This is a very important law, and is also a culminating statement. To be Maa Kheru, or to speak truth, is the ultimate goal of every Initiate. The Initiate must strive to always be as realistic as possible. However, it is important to understand the qualifications for this as well. You should not intentionally tell a lie, nor should you speak that which you have no knowledge of. If you don't know, say that you don't know. However, in a time when your speaking of the truth may lead to the unwarranted harm of another, keep your mouth closed, and if forced to speak, your saying anything, but the truth will be considered speaking truth. Understand that Truth is Maat, which is law, which is love, which is evolution. However, the Initiate must always keep abreast of the consequences of all his words that come out of his mouth. For example, is it lawful to tell someone the whereabouts of your loved one, if you know that they have the intention to harm them? Could such an act of "speaking truth" really be considered lawful or love? In a situation like that it would be best to be silent, for in doing so you will ultimately be found innocent.

Chapter 10

I HAVE NOT CARRIED OFF GOODS BY FORCE

One must not steal another person's property. Thou shalt not steal land or clothes or food or shelter or anything else, for that matter, that does not belong to them. There is a huge 'cause and effect' debt which is created in the Earth when one steals. This debt will be paid eventually, and if not by you, then it is passed on to your bloodline.

Chapter 11

I HAVE NOT UTTERED VILE OR EVIL WORDS

Understand the creative power of the Word. It all begins with the Word. If you wish to maintain order in the family, and the community, be mindful of your speech. Do not fall for the tricks of the foreign cultures. The foreigners have it all wrong with this concept of "freedom of speech." Your speech is only free, if it is in the best interest of the whole community, otherwise censorship is just and due. Filth and evil, Isfet, should not be in our minds, not even in our mouths. However, if this is going on, we must make every effort to check it before it rolls off our tongue. Therefore, think five times before you speak. Don't just talk without thinking. Pay attention to what you are saying for it can assist in the investigation into what is inside of you.

Chapter 12

I HAVE NOT CARRIED OFF FOOD BY FORCE

One must not steal another person's property. Thou shalt not steal land or clothes or food or shelter or anything else, for that matter, that does not belong to them. There is a huge 'cause and effect' debt which is created on Earth when one steals. This debt will be paid eventually, and if not by you, then it is passed on to your bloodline.

Chapter 13

I HAVE NOT EATEN
MY HEART

A man or woman must not lose their temperament and Self Control, as the heart is a symbol for the Will, the mind, conscience, and compassion. The Ab, the heart, is the major component of the spirit that distinguishes man from the rest of creation. To have the heart eaten or devoured was one of the main consequences of living a life contrary to Maat, the Law of Neter. The animal that devoured the heart, after death, was called Ammit, and it was symbolized by a composite animal. The Ammit was a blend of many different beasts, some of which were also the representation of various Neteru. This is significant for it is the Will that allows you to control your animating forces, the Neteru, which prevents them from operating in chaos and enslaving you. Therefore this declaration is ultimately a statement of maintaining Self Control, as well as a clean conscious. To lose control is to give the animal spirit control over your intentions, likes and dislikes. When we do that we become victim to the whims and nefarious agendas of others. They do this by controlling our animal spirit.

I HAVE NOT INVADED ANY MAN'S LAND

Chaos is created when one invades another man's land. It is very critical to maintain a positive 'cause and effect' debt, as a nation. It is important that we respect everyone and their boundaries. One of the chief purposes of justice is to ensure that things do not infringe upon one another, and each thing has its place in the sun. This has been a difficult lesson for man to learn, for history is full of colonialism, imperialism, and mass-genocide by way of invading other people's land. This is also one of the major reasons why the demise of the people that have committed such acts is inevitable. No one can escape 'cause and effect' and justice. Therefore it is wise to find your own place in the sun and do well to be content and work with it. If a time comes where expansion is necessary, go about it in the most honourable and diplomatic way. Maintain the integrity of the nation, and yourself.

Chapter 15

I HAVE NOT SLAUGHTERED ANIMALS WHICH BELONG TO NETER

All animals belong to Neter, and are expressions of Neter. They are another means through which the creator comes into being and experiences itself. They should be respected as expressions of Neter. Animals operate by the dictates of nature. On the other hand, nature maintains population control by means of the mating seasons, as well as the food chain of the animal kingdom. Maat is evolution, which can manifest as creation, as well as extinction. That being said, nature does not need our assistance, as humans, in killing animals. We should not just arbitrarily kill animals for sport, nor should we arbitrarily kill them for sacrifice. The only time when the killing of an animal is permitted, is in self-defence and to preserve the security of the nation or yourself. Maat is also order and balance. This means that even in killing animals, the balance and harmony which exists in the ecosystem must not be violated. It must be maintained at all times, for to destroy it, would be to subsequently destroy ourselves.

Chapter 16

I HAVE NOT LAID WASTE THE LANDS WHICH HAVE BEEN PLOUGHED

An Initiate must view this declaration, or law, in different angles. First there is the literal interpretation, in which it speaks to destroying the useful land, and the work and fruit thereof. This can be tied into the declaration regarding invading another's land. To plough the land requires work. It requires time and sacrifice of the life-force. Someone invested the time and effort, and the work to build up the land, and develop the nation. In the same way that you would not want one to destroy what you have built, especially in righteousness, the same attitude should be held towards others and their work and possessions. Secondly, this declaration, or law, also speaks to what is called the Law of Use. If you've been given something by destiny, your life-path, use it, maintain it, respect it, and evolve it. The ignoring of this law is one of the surest ways to ensure that what you are wasting, not putting to use, will be taken away from you. Whether it be land, love, or a talent, if you don't use it, you will lose it.

Chapter 17

I HAVE NOT PRIED INTO MATTERS TO MAKE MISCHIEF

One's intentions are always to be contemplated upon to see if they are just and positively fruitful to the whole community. If you do not mean well, stay out of it. In all things, one must respect another person's boundaries. Mischief making, is one of the chief indicators of a being not in control of their Will.

Chapter 18

I HAVE NOT SET MY MOUTH IN MOTION AGAINST ANY MAN

Speak truth, but make sure that it is truth before you speak. Do not speak against someone unless it is true and in the best interest of the whole. This has been an issue in many communities. People are afraid to speak the truth, when they know someone has done something wrong. You do not want to be considered a spy, and as a result the disease and chaos spreads. It is fuelled by your actions of letting the evil go uncorrected. Maat is about correction and removing the diseases that are killing the whole community. As the Kamitic saying goes "evil rises when good people remain silent." What this Law of Neter, or declaration is referring to, is speaking against someone without just cause, and with malice in mind. If you do not care for someone, it would be wise to not speak their name.

Chapter 19

I HAVE NOT GIVEN WAY TO WRATH WITHOUT DUE CAUSE

Within the African context we declare that peace is our nature. However, everything that exists has its proper place and time, as well as purpose. One must not confuse passivity with peace. If someone invades your home and attacks you and your family what are you going to do? Are you going to sit there and remain peaceful, meditate, and enjoy the peace, while they have their way? Would you joyfully watch another attack your wife and children? Would you maintain your peace and smile while your husband beats you? Of course not. That is not the Way of Maat. There is a time for wrath, war, violence, and anger. You must maintain and protect what you love. "Fight or Flight" is a natural response of the animating principle that allows us to exist within this realm. Have you ever seen an animal laugh or remain peaceful when it is being attacked? This must be said for it has been the plight of the oppressed to love the oppressor and their oppression. This, in and of itself, is a violation of Maat. However, understand that in all things, one must maintain Self Control. When the time comes for certain things to arise, and for certain emotions to surface, it is your choice to allow them to flow naturally.

Balancing the flow of the lifeforce is the key.

Do not lose yourself in emotions. Anger is channelled and transmuted, it is harnessed and tempered, to defend oneself. All the while the Initiate must maintain control of the energy. The Initiate must look at the present order of things, the condition of the people. The energy of revolution is in the world. It is an energy of anger and frustration that arises out of the dissatisfaction of the people, that gives birth to revolution. Within this word Revolution is Evolution, which is law, which is love. The problem comes with the second part of the declaration, or law, which is to anger without reason. The anger problem, is where one becomes angry at anything, big or small, this is to be avoided and corrected. Reason must be maintained, at all times. Temperance and balance are always to be contemplated upon.

Chapter 20

I HAVE NOT COMMITTED FORNICATION

Traditionally, in the illustrious African culture of Kamit, when a man and a woman engage in sexual intercourse it constituted marriage and responsibility. This kept the moral fabric of the community intact. The idea of sex with "no strings attached" leads to over-indulgence with multiple partners, the spread of disease, and ultimately a decline in the discipline and moral integrity of the people. It is understood by the African culture of Kamit that when the two of you come together, you are bringing your African Ancestors with you. You are like a chemist mixing chemicals as you join your chemistries together. You do not solely belong to you from a personal perspective. You are a culmination of your African Ancestors and you exist as a multiplicity of entities. So when indulging in sexual relationships, understand that you are using something that belongs to your Shepsu, your Ancestors, as well. Just as in all things that you do, you must keep your Ancestors in mind. That is to say, you must respect your body, for it "houses" your Shepsu and the Neteru.

Chapter 21

I HAVE NOT COMMITTED GENDER BASED VIOLENCE

In African culture, tradition, history and spirituality, the act of gender based violence is a violation of all the Laws of Neter. Neter is life. Life is evolution. It is about perpetuating and maintaining life. The act of gender based violence is a clear violation of Maat and the laws of nature. It is considered taboo in authentic African culture as it leads to chaos (Isfet). Everything has a form and a function that is meant to sustain and evolve life. Such an act is not the Way of Maat. It is chaos. It is also evident that, by design, man and woman were created to come together and live as equals. This is the true meaning of African Spirituality (**AS**): Harmony, balance, order, prosperity and reciprocity in the family and among all relationships. When it happens, in due season, that coming together brings creation and evolution. It is a testament to the fact that male-female relationships are based on Maat - the Laws of Neter - and our forms and functions speak to that truth. However, it must be understood that Maat is evolution which manifests as creation, and since gender based violence cannot lead to creation, it leads to destruction and extinction. Those that engage in such destruction corrupt and curse their bloodline, as this perpetuates a cycle of violence, self-hate and disorder. To that end, for some people, this is a life-path challenge that they face, but can be overcome if they choose to live by Maat. In ancient advanced cultures and spirituality, it is said one can tell the health of a society based on the treatment of women and children. A society prone to gender based violence is a sick society that needs healing. That healing starts inside each and every individual by adopting and living the Way of Maat.

Chapter 22

I HAVE NOT POLLUTED MYSELF

Your body is literally a Het Neter, a house that shelters the Neter within. No man or woman is an island. You belong to not only Self, Neter, but also your Shepsu, Ancestors. Whatever you take in mentally, spiritually and physically, ultimately becomes a part of you. Therefore, to maintain and improve the quality of life for your Self, Neter, as well as your Shepsu, Ancestors, you must always consume the best, on all levels.

Chapter 23

I HAVE NOT SLAIN THE WIFE OF A MAN

Simplifying and repeating is a way of learning for the Initiate. It must be emphasised again, slaying a man or a woman is a grave act with major repercussions. The unwarranted murder of any person is a grave mistake, and places one in a position of major 'cause and effect' debt. Even in acts of Self-defence, murder should be the absolute last resort, and it should be something that one should try at all cost to avoid. Self-defence is the only allowance in this law, and one should never be the aggressor.

Chapter 24

I HAVE NOT MADE ANY MAN AFRAID

Fear is a disease. It is literally a dis-ease. It is a disturbance in the homeostasis of one's being. This deviation reverts the person to the negative expression of their animal principle within. It depletes the life-force. It must be understood that there are only two forces in the world and that is Love and Fear. Fear is an expression of the Ego, Set, and Love is an expression of the Self, Ausar. So it should be the goal of the Initiate to invoke the Love of Self and one another, instead of Fear and Ego. However, the majority of the uninitiated operate on fear and insecurity. The Initiate must be conscious of this state of being. However, when the Initiate has strayed off the path or has become stagnated, the Shepsu, Ancestors, and Neteru may use Fear to correct them. Everything has its place in space and time.

Chapter 25

I HAVE NOT MADE MY SPEECH TO BURN WITH ANGER

Speech, words are meant to convey or transport ideas, however, when you are speaking from a place of anger, most times you are not thinking before speaking, and what you are trying to convey is destroyed, burned by the anger. The message cannot be heard over the negative emotion, and yelling. The person you are speaking to goes into defence mode, which is an expression of the animal principle within, which shuts off the higher reasoning mental faculties and does not allow them to process what is being said. This being the case, it is wise to take some time to calm down before getting into a heated discussion. In so doing, it will preserve the relationship between you and the individuals involved. That is why it is said that a person's ruin lies in their tongue. If we speak in anger we ruin the relationships around us. Hence, one must wait for the heart to calm down properly before they dare open their mouth.

Chapter 26

I HAVE NOT MADE MYSELF DEAF TO THE WORDS OF RIGHT AND TRUTH

Ignoring the truth and doing something wrong when you know better speaks to Set being in control of your being. It reflects that you have consciously chosen to walk the dark side of life. One would only choose to ignore the truth or do the wrong thing, to preserve some selfish ambition of theirs, and to gratify their Ego. This is not the Way of Maat. If you know better, do better.

Chapter 27

I HAVE NOT MADE ANOTHER PERSON TO WEEP

Causing another to weep is similar to causing another to fear. It causes disease in the life-force, and should be avoided at all cost. The ultimate goal is the love for your fellow brothers and sisters. It is also to have good intentions for them, as much as you have good intentions for yourself.

Chapter 28

I HAVE NOT UTTERED BLASPHEMY

Once again you must understand the power of the Word, as well as respect all life. The story of the Destruction of Mankind tells of Ra, the Father of the Neteru, ordering the destruction of mankind because of their blasphemies and disrespect of him. Remember, All is a transformation and expression of Ra, therefore All must be respected and viewed with reverence for the Neter within. Also, the Hieroglyph for Ra is the Mouth, in which the Word or Sound emits from. It represents the sounds, words, by which all things function. If one chooses not to function or vibrate on the proper frequency, then it causes deviation and perversion, which in and of itself, is a blasphemy and abuse of Ra.

Chapter 29

I HAVE NOT ACTED WITH VIOLENCE

Simplifying and repeating is a way of learning for the Initiate. It must be emphasised again, that violence is a grave act with major repercussions. Unwarranted violence towards any person or living thing is a grave mistake, and places one in a position of major 'cause and effect' debt. Even in acts of Self-defence, violence should be in good measure and well calculated.

Chapter 30

I HAVE NOT ACTED WITHOUT DUE CONSIDERATION

Many people cause the most damage, and end up with deep regret, when they allow themselves to act without thinking. In all things let your reason be your guide. Contemplate the matter in front of you. Think five times before you act, consider all foreseeable possibilities, but do it swiftly.

I HAVE NOT PIERCED, MORTIFIED MY SKIN AND TAKEN VENGEANCE AGAINST NETER

Altering yourself physically, out of dissatisfaction with the way that Neter made you, is Isfet, chaos, and it is not the Way of Maat. People indulge all kinds of cosmetic surgeries done to compensate for the so-called "mistakes" and inadequacies that they perceive Neter made. Such chaos can be seen in these Deeds and Words, "Neter made a mistake when Neter made me Black, so I will bleach my skin to remove this Blackness." Such chaos can lead to the manifestation of a depressed life-force, which creates more chaos in the person's life, such as self-hatred or more self-mutilation. It can ultimately lead to the unwarranted death of the person, psychologically or physically, caused by the mutilation. In all things, one must cultivate understanding, and a feeling of gratitude, and appreciate Neter, and recognize the beautiful masterpiece that Neter created when you came into being.

Chapter 32

I HAVE NOT MULTIPLIED MY SPEECH BEYOND WHAT SHOULD BE SAID

When speaking, be careful of saying too much or exaggerating. Speak truth. Know when to come and know when to go. Know when to talk and when to listen. Know what to say and how much to say in all matters of conversations. This understanding is cultivated through deep contemplation and practice. Watch your words, see how they create and make sure they bear fruits that heal others, including yourself.

Chapter 33

I HAVE NOT COMMITTED FRAUD AND LOOKED UPON EVIL

Hear no evil, see no evil, speak no evil, and only open the door to Maat - the way of truth and order. Do not allow yourself to engage in or watch that which should not be done. Remember that the spirit is receptive, and you do not wish to pollute it with filth or chaos. Your ears and eyes are doors to your inner Neter. Guard these doors with your life and only open them to what heals and builds. Only the Way of Maat builds a life of peace and joy. Peace is healing and joy is nurturing. Anything else will build Isfet, disorder and evil. Your Attention is a very important treasure, only pay Attention to words and images that will heal and build you. Simply walk away from things that are soiled with Isfet.

Chapter 34

I HAVE NOT UTTERED CURSES AGAINST THE KING

In Ancient Africa, African people always knew and understood that no man makes himself a King. He is chosen by the Ancestors, and ordained by Neter, based upon his state of evolution. Therefore, throughout African culture you see the Divine Kingship. The Divine King is not interested in you worshiping him, or being a slave. He is not a tyrant, but rather is a servant that works for you, Neter, and the Ancestors, Paut Shepsu. He is a symbol of them on Earth. Therefore, if he does something or makes a decision that you do not like or understand, be patient with him. Ask him to explain his reasoning, speak with the Ancestors, consult an Oracle or speak with the Elders. But do not wage a public war of words on the Man that the Ancestors, Shepsu, have ordained as King. As long as he is a Righteous King, have patience with him. That is the Way of Maat.

Chapter 35

I HAVE NOT FOULED RUNNING WATER

Water is the essence of life, and all life depends on it. When water sits, it becomes stale and poisonous. Therefore all over the earth, running water is a treasure and blessing to have. This being said, take care of it, do not pollute it with waste. This also speaks to your internal running water, which is your blood and vital fluids. Do not defile it with improper behaviour and diet. Appreciate life and appreciate the fluids that flow within your body. Do not pollute them with harmful food.

Chapter 36

I HAVE NOT EXALTED MY SPEECH

Do not yell at people, speak peacefully, calmly and smile. Speak clearly, patiently and with confidence. When communicating, it is wise to make an effort to make the other person feel important and comfortable with you. This is how to properly handle people. It doesn't matter if you are in a higher position or have authority over them, treat them with respect and honour.

Chapter 37

I HAVE NOT UTTERED CURSES AGAINST NETER

None but the pure must approach the pure. In African culture the Word is viewed as the Creative agent in the world. It is sound vibrations that move things and create change. In our sacred stories, it is through the speaking of the Name of the various Neteru by Ra that brings them into existence. Ra says, "I brought into my mouth my own name, that is to say, Hekau, a word of power, and I, even I, came into being in the form of Kheperu, in the form of things which came into being, and I came into being ..." If words are creative, then what comes out of your mouth must be treated with great care. It must be clean. It must be purified. Pure. When speaking to others, or even engaging in thinking, your words must be pure, clean. Your words are sacred. That is to say, your words and thoughts must be grounded in Maat. Pure words will result in pure creation. Maat creates Maat. Chaos causes chaos. Neter is the Whole. The parts are expressions of Neter, the Whole. Each person that you meet is an expression of Neter. Hence, one must never utter curses against any one, it is the same as uttering curses to the Whole itself, which is Neter. Conversely, one must never insult the Whole, Neter, for it would be the same as insulting the Parts, your Self.

I HAVE NOT BEHAVED WITH INSOLENCE

Arrogance is an expression of the Ego, Set. It is where Heru meets Set and you cannot tell the difference. Enlightenment brings humility and compassion, so these are the traits that every African wants to cultivate. Remember this, no matter how great, smart, good looking you are, if you do not know how to treat people you are nothing. No man is an island. In African wisdom, a child is raised by the whole village.

Chapter 39

I HAVE NOT BEEN GUILTY OF FAVOURITISM

Be just. Do not cheat someone simply because you favour another over them. Prejudice and bias, tip the scales in our decision making, and clouds our perception which disallows us to see clearly. This can lead to our demise down the line. If you separate or make distinctions between things, they should be based upon Maat, efficiency and principle, and not on favouritism and bias. Make decisions based on Maat. Maat creates Maat.

Chapter 40

I HAVE NOT INCREASED MY WEALTH EXCEPT BY MEANS OF SUCH THINGS THAT ARE MY OWN

Again, simplifying and repeating is the best way that the spirit of the Initiate learns. It is considered as if one is injecting wisdom directly into the blood of the Initiate. As stated in the preceding laws, "unwarranted" theft is regarded as Isfet, chaos. Theft in general, like violence, is considered unwarranted. As a person, you should attempt to exhaust all possibilities, and your faculties and capabilities before resorting to theft. Remember that, All is an expression of Neter and that includes you, and what you do to another you do to Self, you do to Neter. You must think about the effect of your actions in the grand scheme of life. How will my taking of this sister's bread affect her? How will it affect her family? How will it affect my spiritual growth and development? Is this the only solution? One must think first and deeply, and try to intuit alternatives.

Chapter 41

I HAVE NOT UTTERED CURSES AGAINST THE THINGS THAT BELONG TO NETER AND ARE WITH ME

Your words are sacred. That is to say, your words and thoughts must be grounded in Maat. Pure words will result in pure creation. Maat creates Maat. That is, order creates order. Isfet causes Isfet. That is, chaos causes chaos. Neter is the Whole. The Parts are expressions of Neter, the Whole. Each person or thing that you meet is an expression of Neter. Hence, one must never utter curses against anything or anyone for that matter. It would be the same as uttering curses to the Whole itself, which is Neter. Conversely, one must never insult the Whole, Neter, for it would be the same as insulting the Parts, your Self.

Chapter 42

I HAVE NOT HARBOURED SCORNFUL THOUGHTS ABOUT THE NETERU

Understand that the natural flow of the universe is evolution, and in all things there is a reason and a lesson. Everything that we see is a manifestation of the Neteru, forces of nature. Everything that takes place is a particular Neter, force of nature, behind the scenes moving things. Knowing this, one can run the risk of becoming angry or dissatisfied with the way that the spirit is moving. Instead of allowing the negative emotion to take control, ask for understanding and work to intuit how what is happening fits into the grand scheme of things. See the Big Picture and try to make changes based on what you clearly see, from a pure heart, not from negative emotions. Be patient and seek wise counsel about the situation. Consult the Elders or an Oracle, and then make a decision based on their wisdom. Tehuti is also known as "Neb Metu Neter." That is, he is "Lord of the Words of the forces of nature." Let him reveal to you the Truth.

Chapter X

EPILOGUE

After reading the Book of Maat, the Prince, Setna, was pleased with himself, that after this long he was still able to learn so much from it. He said, "I am the pure Lotus which springs up from the divine splendour that belongs to the nostrils of Ra. I have made my way, and I follow on seeking for him who is Heru. I am the pure one who comes forth out of the Field." Even though, he reads the Book at least twice a day, and declares to his spirit that he has not violated any of these Ancient Laws of Maat, which have stood the test of time, he was still able to get new insights. It gave him confidence that when the time comes for him to pass on to the Duat, his Ab, heart, will not be devoured by Ammit, the beast. Instead his heart, will be as light as the Feather of Maat during the day of his heart being weighed. Furthermore, he understood that this judgement happens at every crossroad of life, when one has to make a choice between Maat and Isfet, between right and wrong. Perusing the Book of Maat, daily, allowed and reminded him to stay focused, and stay hungry for more wisdom. The Book of Maat nurtured, nourished and healed his spirit on a daily basis. It made him understand that Maat was unmistakably the guiding laws to live one's life by. Maat was the natural laws that created order, harmony and balance in the universe, and within society. Maat was the very foundation that Neter created the universe upon, and it was advisable for mankind to use these very laws to govern society and the individuals that live therein.

BOOK OF AFRICAN SPIRITUALITY

Book of Ausar

Chapter 0

A CURSE ON NUT

1. In the days before Ra had left the earth, before he had begun to grow old, his great wisdom told him that if the Neter Nut bore children, one of them would end his reign among men. So Ra laid a curse upon Nut, that she should not be able to bear any child upon any day in the year.

2. Full of sorrow, Nut went for help to Tehuti, the great Neter of wisdom and hekau and learning, Ra's son, who loved her. Tehuti knew that the curse of Ra, once spoken, could never be recalled, but in his wisdom he found a way of escape. He went to Khonsu, the Moon-Neter, and challenged him to a contest at Senet. Game after game they played and Tehuti always won. The stakes grew higher and higher, but Khonsu wagered the most, for it was some of his own light that he risked and lost.

3. At last Khonsu would play no more. Then Tehuti the thrice-great in wisdom gathered up the light which he had won and made it into five extra days which, forever after, were set between the end of the old year and the beginning of the new. The year was of three hundred and sixty days before

this, but the five days which were added, which were not days of any year, were ever afterwards, held as days of festival in old Kamit.

4. But, since his match with Tehuti, Khonsu the moon has not had enough light to shine throughout the month, but dwindles into darkness and then grows to his full glory again, for he had lost the light needed to make five whole days.

5. On the first of these days Ausar, the eldest son of Nut, was born, and the second day was set aside to be the birthday of Heru the Elder. On the third day, the third son of Nut was born, Set, the lord of Isfet. On the fourth, her daughter Auset first saw the light, and her second daughter Nebt Het on the fifth. In this way the curse of Ra was both fulfilled and defeated, for the days on which the children of Nut were born belonged to no year.

Chapter 1

BOOK OF KNOWING THE EVOLUTIONS OF AUSAR AND THE OVERCOMING OF SET

1. When Ausar was born many signs and wonders were seen and heard throughout the world. Most notable was the voice which came from the holiest shrine in the temple at Thebes on the Nile, which today is called Karnak, speaking to a sage bidding him proclaim to all men that Ausar, the good and mighty king, was born to bring joy to all the earth. The sage did as he was bidden, and he also attended on the Divine Child and brought him up as a man among men.

2. When Ausar was grown up he married Auset, as he was a Neter, he could only marry another Neter. And Set married Nebt Het for he too being a Neter could marry only a Neter.

3. After Auset, had learned the Secret Name of Ra, Ausar became sole ruler of Kamit and reigned on earth as Ra had done. He found the people both savage and brutish, fighting among themselves

and killing one another. But Auset discovered the grain of both wheat and barley, which grew wild over the land with the other plants and was still unknown to man.

4.   Ausar taught them how to plant the seeds when the Nile had risen in the yearly inundation and sunk again leaving fresh fertile mud over the fields, how to tend and water the crops, how to cut the corn when it was ripe, and how to thresh the grain on the threshing floors, dry it and grind it to flour and make it into bread. He showed them also how to plant vines and make the grapes into wine, and they knew already how to brew beer out of the barley.

5.   When the people of Kamit had learned to make bread and cut only the flesh of such animals as he taught them were suitable, Ausar, went on to teach them laws, and how to live peacefully and happily together, delighting themselves with music and poetry.

6.   As soon as Kamit was filled with peace and plenty, Ausar set out over the world to bring his blessings upon other nations. While he was away he left Auset to rule over the land, which she did both wisely and well.

7.   But Set the Evil One, their brother, envied Ausar and hated Auset. The more the people loved and praised Ausar, the more Set hated him, and the more good he did and the happier mankind became, the stronger grew Set's desire to kill his brother and rule in his place.

8.   Auset, however, was so full of wisdom and so watchful that Set made no attempt to seize the

throne while she was watching over the land of Kamit.

9. And when Ausar returned from his travels Set was among the first to welcome him back and kneel in reverence before "the good Neter Nesu Ausar."

10. Yet he had made his plans, aided by seventy-two of his wicked friends. Secretly Set obtained the exact measurements of the body of Ausar, and caused a beautiful chest to be made that would fit only him. It was fashioned of the rarest and most expensive wood: cedar brought from the East, and ebony from Punt at the south end of the Red Sea for no strong wood grows in Kamit except the soft and fragile kind.

11. Then Set gave a great feast in honour of Ausar, but the other guests were the seventy two conspirators. It was the greatest feast that had yet been seen in Kamit, and the foods were choicer, the wines stronger and the dancing girls more beautiful than ever before. Set knew how to party. When the heart of Ausar had been made glad with feasting and song the chest was brought in, and all were amazed at its beauty.

12. Ausar marvelled at the rare cedar inlaid with ebony and ivory, with rare gold and silver, and painted inside with figures of Neteru and birds and animals, and he desired it greatly.

13. "I will give this chest to whosoever fits it most exactly!" cried Set. And at once the conspirators began in turn to see if they could win it. But one was too tall and another too short, one was too fat and another too thin, and all tried in vain.

14. "Let me see if I will fit into this marvellous piece of work," said Ausar, and he laid himself down

in the chest while all gathered round breathlessly. "I fit exactly, and the chest is mine!" cried Ausar. "And the chest is mine!"

15. "It is yours indeed, and shall be so forever!" hissed Set as he banged down the lid. Then in desperate haste, he and the conspirators nailed it shut and sealed every crack with molten lead, so that Ausar the man died in the chest and his spirit went west across the Nile into Amenti.

16. Set and his companions took the chest which held the body of Ausar and cast it into the Nile, and Hapi the Nile-Neter carried it out into the Great Green Sea where it was tossed for many days until it came to the shore of Phoenicia near the city of Byblos.

17. In Byblos, the waves cast it into a tamarisk tree that grew on the shore, and the tree shot out branches and grew leaves and flowers to make a fit resting place for the body of the good Neter Ausar, and soon enough the tree became famous throughout the land.

18. Presently the King of Byblos heard of it, and he and his wife, the Queen, came to the seashore to gaze at the tree. By now the branches had grown together and hidden the chest which held the body of Ausar in the trunk itself. The King gave orders that the tree should be cut down and fashioned into a great pillar for his palace. This was done, and all wondered at its beauty and fragrance: but none knew that it held the body of a Neter.

19. Meanwhile in Kamit, Auset was in great fear. She had always known that Set was filled with evil and jealousy, but kindly Ausar would not believe in his brother's wickedness. But Auset knew as soon

as her husband was dead, though no one told her, and fled into the marshes of the delta.

20. Then she went to look for the body of Ausar. For, until he was buried with all the needful rites and heka, even his spirit could go no farther to the west in Amenti.

21. Back and forth over the land of Kamit wandered Auset, but never a trace could she find of the chest in which lay the body of Ausar. She asked all whom she met, but no one had seen it, and in this matter her Hekau powers could not help her.

22. At last she questioned the children who were playing by the riverside, and at once they told her that just such a chest as she described had floated past them on the swift stream and out into the Great Green Sea.

23. Then Auset wandered on the shore, and again and again it was the children who had seen the chest floating by and told her which way it had gone. And because of this, Auset blessed the children and decreed that ever afterwards children should speak words of wisdom and sometimes tell of things to come.

24. At last, Auset came to Byblos and sat down by the seashore. Presently, the maidens who attended on the Queen of Byblos came down to bathe at that place, and when they returned out of the water Auset taught them how to plait their hair - which had never been done before. When they went up to the palace a strange and wonderful perfume seemed to cling to them, and the Queen of Byblos marvelled at it, and at their plaited hair, and asked them how it came to be so.

25. The maidens told her of the wonderful woman who sat by the seashore, and the Queen of Byblos sent for Auset, and asked her to serve in the palace and tend her children, the little Prince and the baby, who was ailing sorely. For she did not know that the strange woman who was wandering alone at Byblos was the greatest of all the Neteru of Kamit.

26. Auset agreed to serving in the palace, and very soon the baby was strong and well though she did no more than give him her finger to suck. But presently she became fond of the child, and thought to make him immortal, which she did by burning away his mortal parts while she flew round and round him in the form of a swallow. The Queen of Byblos, however, had been watching her secretly, and when she saw that her baby seemed to be on fire she rushed into the room with a loud cry, and so broke the Hekau powers.

27. Then Auset took on her own form, and the Queen of Byblos crouched down in terror when she saw the shining Neter and learned who she was.

28. The King and Queen of Byblos offered her gifts of all the richest treasures in Byblos, but Auset asked only for the great tamarisk pillar which held up the roof, and for what it contained. When it was given to her, she caused it to open and took out the chest of Set. But she gave back the pillar to the King and Queen of Byblos, and it remained the most sacred object in Byblos, since it had once held the body of a Neter.

29. When the chest which had become the coffin of Ausar was given to her, Auset flung herself down on it with so terrible a cry of sorrow that the little

baby died at the very sound. But Auset, at length, caused the chest to be placed on a ship which the King of Byblos provided for her, and set out for Kamit.

30. With her, went the young prince of Byblos. But he did not remain with her for long, since his curiosity proved his undoing. For as soon as the ship had left the land, Auset retired to where the chest of Ausar lay, and opened the lid. The young prince of Byblos crept up behind her and peeped over her shoulder. But Auset knew he was there and, turning, gave him one glance of anger - and he fell backwards over the side of the ship into the sea.

31. Next morning, as the ship was passing the Phaedrus River, its strong current threatened to carry them out of sight of land. But Auset grew angry and placed a curse on the river, so that its stream dried up from that day.

32. When Auset came safely to the land of Kamit, she took the body and transformed herself into a swallow. She then hovered over the body, causing a wind with her wings, and raised the phallus of the body, and received his seed. Thus was Heru conceived.

33. She then hid the chest in the marshes of the delta. She found shelter on a little island in Buto, and entrusted the Divine Child, Heru, to a woman from there. And as a further safeguard against Set, Auset loosened the island from its foundations, and let it float so that no one could tell where to find it.

34. But it chanced that Set came hunting wild boars with his dogs, hunting by night after his custom,

since he loved the darkness in which evil things abound. By the light of the moon he saw the chest of cedar wood inlaid with ebony and ivory, with gold and silver, and recognised it.

35. At the sight, hatred and anger came upon him in a red cloud, and he raged like a panther of the south. He tore open the chest, took the body of Ausar, and cut it into fourteen pieces which, by his divine strength, he scattered up and down the whole length of the Nile so that the crocodiles might eat them.

36. "It is not possible to destroy the body of a Neter!" cried Set. "Yet I have done it - for I have destroyed Ausar!" His laughter echoed through the land, and all who heard it trembled and hid.

37. Now Auset had to begin her search once more. This time she had helpers, for Nebt Het left her wicked husband Set and came to join her sister. And Anpu, the son of Ausar and Nebt Het, taking the form of a jackal, assisted in the search.

38. When Auset travelled over the land she was accompanied and guarded by seven scorpions. But when she searched on the Nile and among the many streams of the delta, she made her way in a boat made of papyrus. The crocodiles, in their reverence for the Neter, did not touch the boat. Indeed ever afterwards anyone who sailed the Nile in a boat made of papyrus was safe from them, for they thought that it was Auset still questing after the pieces of her husband's body.

39. Slowly, piece by piece, Auset recovered the fragments of Ausar. And wherever she did so, she formed by Hekau the likeness of his whole body and caused the priests to build a shrine

and perform his funeral rites. And so there were thirteen places in Kamit which claimed to be the burial place of Ausar. In this way also she made it harder for Set to meddle further with the body of the dead Neter.

40. However, she did not recover one piece, for it had been eaten by certain impious fishes, and their kind were accursed ever afterwards, and no Kamityu would touch or eat them.

41. Auset, however, did not bury any of the pieces in the places where the tombs and shrines of Ausar stood. She gathered the pieces together, rejoined them by Hekau, and by Hekau made a likeness of the missing member so that Ausar was complete. Then she caused the body to be embalmed and hidden away in a place of which she alone knew. And after this the spirit of Ausar passed deep into Amenti to rule over the dead until the last great battle, when Heru should slay Set and Ausar would return to earth once more.

42. But as Heru grew in this world the spirit of Ausar visited him often and taught him all that a great warrior should know. One strategy which he taught him was how to fight against Set both in the body and in the spirit.

43. One day Ausar said to the boy: "Tell me, what is the noblest thing that a man can do?" And Heru answered: "To honour your African Ancestors." This pleased Ausar, and he asked further: "And how do you honour them?" "By learning about and practising their History, Culture, Tradition and Spirituality," replied Heru, "by also building a shrine for them and the Neteru and feeding their

Kau, with candlelight, water, food and incense, to say the least."

44. When he heard this, his heart was pleased. But he was not done yet, so he posed another question to him: "What is the libation that must be used for me?" And Heru answered: "This is your libation, Atef. This is your libation, from your mesu. To make a libation of the North, round about, coming from your mesu, coming from Heru. I have come, I bring you the Eye of Heru, so that your heart may be refreshed by it. I bring it to you to carry you, to be under your soles. I bring you the Eye of Heru which is on your brow. The sound Eye of Heru is being rubbed on your face. You awake in peace. The Neter Ausar awakes in peace."

45. When he heard this, Ausar knew that the time had come for Heru to declare war on Set, and bade him gather together a great army and sail up the Nile to attack him in the deserts of the south.

46. Heru gathered his forces and prepared to begin the war. And Ra himself, the shining father of the Neteru, came to his aid in his own divine boat that sails across the heavens and through the dangers of the Duat.

47. Before they set sail, Ra drew Heru aside so as to gaze into his brown eyes, for whoever looks into them, of Neteru or men, sees the future reflected there. But Set was watching, and he took upon himself the form of a black pig, black as the thunder-cloud, fierce to look at, with tusks to strike terror into the bravest heart.

48. Meanwhile Ra said to Heru: "Let me gaze into your eyes, and see what is to come of this war."

He gazed into the eyes of Heru which were now full of wisdom. The kind of wisdom that only belonged to the African Ancestors.

49. While he gazed, the black pig passed by, and distracted his attention, so that he exclaimed: "Look at that! Never have I seen so huge and fierce a pig."

50. And Heru looked, and he did not know that it was Set, but thought it was a wild boar out of the thickets of the north, and he was not ready with a Heka to guard himself against the enemy.

51. Then Set aimed a blow of fire at the eyes of Heru, and Heru cried out in pain and was in a great rage. He knew now that it was Set, but Set had gone on the instant and could not be trapped.

52. Ra caused Heru to be taken into a dark room, where Tehuti healed his eyes, and it was not long before his eyes could see again as clearly as before. When he was recovered, Ra had returned to the sky, but Heru was filled with joy that he could see, once more, and as he set out up the Nile at the head of his army, the country on either side shared his joy and blossomed into spring.

53. There were many battles that ensued, but the last and greatest was at Edfu, where the great Temple of Heru stands to this day, in memory of it. The forces of Set and Heru drew near to one another among the islands and the rapids of the First Cataract of the Nile.

54. Set, in the form of a red hippopotamus of gigantic size, sprang up on the island of Elephantine and uttered a great curse against Heru and against Auset: "Let there come a terrible raging tempest and a mighty flood against my enemies!" he cried,

and his voice was like the thunder rolling across the heavens from the south to the north.

55. At once the storm broke over the boats of Heru and his army, the wind roared and the water was heaped into great waves. But Heru held on his way, his own boat gleaming through the darkness, its prow shining like a ray of the sun.

56. Opposite Edfu, Set turned and stood at bay, straddling the whole stream of the Nile, so huge a red hippopotamus was he. But Heru took upon himself the shape of a handsome young black man, twelve feet in height. His hand held a harpoon thirty feet long with a blade six feet wide at its point of greatest width.

57. Set opened his mighty jaws to destroy Heru and his followers, so that the storm would wreck their boats. But Heru cast his harpoon, and it struck deep into the head of the red hippopotamus, deep into his brain. And that one blow slew Set the great wicked one, the enemy of Ausar and the Neteru - and the red hippopotamus sank dead beside the Nile at Edfu.

58. The storm passed away, the flood sank and the sky was clear and blue once more. Then the people of Edfu came out to welcome Heru the avenger and lead him in triumph to the shrine over which the great Temple of Edfu now stands.

59. They celebrated and sang the song of praise which the priests chanted ever afterwards when the yearly festival of Heru was held at Edfu: "Rejoice, you who dwell in Edfu! Heru the great Neter, the lord of the sky, has slain the enemy of his father! Eat the flesh and drink the blood of the red hippopotamus, burn his bones with fire! Let him

be cut in pieces, and the scraps be given to the cats, and the offal to the reptiles! Glory to Heru of the mighty blow, the brave one, the slayer, the wielder of the Harpoon, the only son of Ausar, Heru of Edfu, Heru the avenger!"

60. But when Heru passed from earth and reigned no more as the Nesu of Kamit, he appeared before the assembly of the Neteru, and Set came also in the spirit, and contended in words for the rule of the world. But not even Tehuti the wise could give judgment. And so it comes about that Heru and Set still contend for the souls of men and for the rule of the world.

61. There were no more battles on the Nile or in the land of Kamit, and Ausar rested quietly in his grave, which Auset admitted was on the island of Philae, the most sacred place of all in the Nile, a few miles upstream from Elephantine.

62. But the Kamityu believed that the Last Battle was still to come, and that Heru would defeat Set in this also. And when Set was destroyed forever, Ausar would rise from the dead and return to earth, bringing with him all those who had been his own faithful followers. For this reason the Kamityu embalmed the dead and set the bodies away beneath towering pyramids of stone and deep in the tomb chambers of western Thebes, so that the blessed souls returning from Amenti should find them ready to enter again, and in them to live for ever on earth under the good Neter Ausar, Auset his queen and their son Heru.

Chapter 2

BOOK OF KNOWING THE EVOLUTIONS OF AUSAR AND THE OVERCOMING OF SET

1. Here begins the cosmology as retold by another African Sage from a different angle.

2. Oh my brothers and my sisters, gather around me that I may tell you the wisdom story of the Before-Time, of the Golden Age when the Neteru walked upon the earth with us.

3. Know then that in those ancient days, long before even the grandfather of our Nesu's grandfather was born, Ausar the great-grandson of Ra sat upon the throne of the Neteru, ruling over the living world as Ra did over the Neteru. He was the first Nesu, and his Queen, Auset, was the first Queen. They ruled for many ages together, for the world was still young and Grandmother Death was not as harsh as she is now.

4. His ways were just and upright, he made sure that Maat remained in balance, that the law was kept. And so Maat smiled upon the world. All peoples

praised Ausar and Auset, and peace reigned over all, for this was the Golden Age.

5. Yet there was trouble. Proud Set, noble Set, the brother of Ausar, he who defended the Sun Boat from Apep the Destroyer, was unsettled in his heart. He coveted the throne of Ausar. He coveted Auset. He coveted the power over the living world and he desired to take it from his brother.

6. In his dark mind he conceived of a plot to kill Ausar and take it all from him. He built a coffin and inscribed it with wicked Hekau that would chain anyone who entered it from escaping.

7. Set took the coffin to the great feast of the Neteru. He waited until Ausar had made himself drunk on much beer, then challenged Ausar to a contest of strength. Each one in turn would enter the coffin, and attempt, through sheer strength, to break it open.

8. Ausar, sure in his power, yet feeble in mind because of his drink, entered the coffin. Set quickly poured molten lead into the coffin. Ausar tried to escape, but the wicked Hekau held him bound and he died.

9. Set then picked up the box and hurled it into the Nile where it floated away.

10. Set claimed the throne of Ausar for himself and demanded that Auset be his Queen. None of the other Neteru dared to stand against him, for he had killed Ausar and could easily do the same to them. Great Ra turned his head aside and mourned, he did not stand against Set.

11. This was the dark time. Set was everything his brother was not. He was cruel and unkind, caring not for the balance of Maat, or for us, the children

of the Neteru. War divided Kamit, and all was lawless while Set ruled. In vain, Africans cried out to Ra, but his heart was hardened by grief, and he would not listen.

12. Only Auset, blessed Auset, remembered us. Only she, was not afraid of Set. She searched all of the Nile for the coffin containing her beloved husband.

13. Finally she found it, in Byblos, lodged in a tamarisk bush that had turned into a mighty tree, for the power of Ausar was still in him, though he lay dead.

14. She tore open the box and wept over the lifeless body of Ausar. She carried the box back to Kamit and placed it in the house of the Neteru.

15. She changed herself into a bird and flew about his body, singing a song of mourning. Then she perched upon him and used a Heka. The spirit of the dead Ausar entered her, and she conceived and bore a son whose destiny would be to avenge his father.

16. She called the Divine Child, Heru, and hid him on an island far away from the gaze of his uncle Set.

17. She then went to Tehuti, wise Tehuti, who knows all secrets, and implored his help. She asked him for Heka that could bring Ausar back to life. Tehuti, lord of knowledge, who brought himself into being by speaking his name, searched through his Book of Hekau.

18. Tehuti knew that Ausar's spirit had departed his body and was lost. To restore Ausar, Tehuti had to remake him so that his spirit would recognize him and rejoin.

19. Tehuti and Auset together created the Ritual of Life, that which allows us to live forever when we die.

20. But before Tehuti could work the Heka, cruel Set discovered them. He stole the body of Ausar and tore it into many pieces, scattering them throughout Kamit. He was sure that Ausar would never be reborn.

21. Yet Auset would not despair. She implored the help of her sister Nebt Het, to guide her and help her find the pieces of Ausar.

22. Long did they search, bringing each piece to Tehuti that he might work Heka upon it.

23. When all the pieces were together, Tehuti went to Anpu, lord of the dead. Anpu sewed the pieces back together, washed the entrails of Ausar, embalmed him, wrapped him in linen, and cast the Ritual of Life.

24. When Ausar's mouth was opened, due to the Ritual of Life, his spirit re-entered him and he lived again.

25. Yet nothing that has died, not even a Neter, may dwell in the land of the living.

26. Ausar went to the Duat, the abode of the dead. Anpu yielded the throne to him and he became the lord of the dead. There he stands in judgment over the souls of the dead. He commends the acts of the just to the Blessed Land, but the wicked he condemns to be devoured by Ammit.

27. When Set heard that Ausar lived again he was wroth, but his anger waned, for he knew that Ausar could never return to the land of the living. Without Ausar, Set believed he would sit on the throne of the Neteru for all time.

28. Yet on a hidden island, Heru, the son of Ausar and Auset, grew to manhood and strength. Set sent many serpents and demons to kill Heru, but he defeated them.

29. When Heru was ready, his mother Auset gave him great Hekau to use against Set, and Tehuti gave him an Eye empowered with Hekau.

30. Heru sought out Set and challenged him for the throne. Set and Heru fought for many days, but in the end Heru defeated Set and castrated him. But Heru, merciful Heru, would not kill Set, for to spill the blood of his uncle would make him no better than he.

31. Even after defeat, Set still maintained his claim to the throne, and Heru lay claim himself as the son of Ausar.

32. The Neteru began to fight amongst each other, those who supported Heru and those who supported Set.

33. Banebdjetet leaped into the middle and demanded that the Neteru end this struggle peacefully or Maat would be imbalanced further. He told the Neteru to seek the council of Nit.

34. Nit, warlike though wise in council, told them that Heru was the rightful heir to the throne. Heru cast Set into the darkness where he lives to this day.

35. And so it is that Heru watches over us while we live, and gives guidance to the Nesu while he lives, and his father Ausar watches over us in the next life. So it is that the Neteru are at peace. So it is that Set, wicked Set, eternally strives for revenge, battling Heru at every turn. When Heru wins, Maat is upheld and the world is at peace. When

Set wins, the world is in turmoil. But we know that dark times do not last forever, and the bright rays of Heru will shine over us again.

36. In the last days, Heru and Set will fight one last time for the world. Heru will defeat Set forever, and Ausar will be able to return to this world. On that day, the Day of Awakening, all the tombs shall open and the just dead shall live again as we do, and all sorrow shall pass away forever.

Chapter 3

BOOK OF KNOWING THE EVOLUTIONS OF AUSAR AND THE OVERCOMING OF SET

1. In the time that Ausar and Auset came to the Beautiful and Sacred Land of Kamit, better described as Ancient Black Kamit, they found the people and the land in a chaotic state. Isfet, chaos, was the disorder of the day. Brother fought brother and sister quarrelled with sister to no fruitful end or purpose. Nothingness prevailed. There were no rules to guide the people and things that were in the Blessed Land. The people had no foundation to stand on.

2. The first thing that Ausar and Auset did was to lay a foundation in Maat. This they were able to do because they came with the sacred Book of Maat which had the wisdom and power to build a whole nation upon. It was said that he who held the book could lead and guide mankind out of savagery and into civilisation by using its spiritual laws. Ausar and his beloved

wife Auset built a great civilisation in Kamit by using the Book of Maat. They taught the people agriculture, husbandry, laws, land management, town planning, architecture, education, health management and other skills that were required to found a great nation. Because of all these skills the nation of Kamit thrived and Ausar and Auset were made King and Queen and thus established a royal bloodline, which united Lower and Upper Kamit. After a long time of peace, prosperity and wellness in Kamit, King Ausar decided to spread the wisdom from the Book of Maat to other lands, near and far. While he was gone he gave rulership to his beloved wife and Queen, Auset.

3. Ausar's peaceful voyages abroad were very successful and people were very receptive to his teachings from the Book of Maat. He taught them a spiritually based way of life which improved the lives of all in these faraway lands.

4. The only drawback from Ausar's travels was that his jealous brother Set plotted against him back at home, and planned to usurp the throne from him upon his return. Set could not achieve his goal while Queen Auset was in charge, she was too clever for him, and so he waited cunningly for the King to return.

5. On the day of Ausar's return, there was great jubilation in the land of Kamit. Such was the joy of the people that a great feast worthy of a spiritual and greatly beloved king was held. Set also attended the great feast.

6. When all the guests were drunk in merriment and wine and beer, Set rang a bell to get everyone's attention. He rang it three times and there was

an immediate silence in the great hall. Then he made a quick announcement, "I have a wonderful surprise for all of you here to see and try on." Immediately after saying this, a gold and bejewelled casket was wheeled into the great hall and placed in front of Set. Everyone in the crowd, including the King and Queen, exclaimed in unison, "Wow!" He said, "Anyone who fits the casket exactly gets to keep it!"

7. Everyone rushed forward to try it. In a short while a long queue of drunk and tipsy people had formed to try on the gold casket. But no one fit the coffin. Some were too short, others too tall. Some were too fat, others were too skinny. Still no one fit the casket. Finally, Set looked at the King and said, "Your Majesty! Why don't you try it?" The King laughed, put his drink down, and went straight to try the casket, and it fit perfectly. Set and his friends immediately rushed forward to shut the coffin, and poured molten lead to seal it completely.

8. The King quickly suffocated inside the casket and lest to say he died in no time, to the shock of everyone who was at the feast. Nonetheless, armed men came in and broke up the party before any of the King's supporters could react. All were effectively subdued by the might of Set and his army.

9. Set and his followers secretly took the casket and threw it into the Nile River. Set then killed all those who knew where the casket was. He trusted no one with the body. He violently took over the rulership of the land of Kamit.

10. With Set's rule, Isfet returned to Kamit. Might ruled over right. Set ruled by the might of the army, not Maat. Disorder became the law of the land. Might, not Maat, took over.

11. In the meantime, the Queen did not feel safe at all. She knew that Set would be threatened by her presence. So she went undercover and vowed to search for his body.

12. The Queen looked all over the land for her husband, to no avail. She asked adults, male and female, about the whereabouts of her King, but none were forthcoming for fear of Set, even the ones who knew. Finally, some children came forth to her secretly, without the knowledge of their parents, and told her that the casket was thrown into the Nile River.

13. On the other side, Set was distracted and carried on with dictatorial and tyrannical rule. This allowed Auset to plan her next moves.

14. Auset, with seven scorpions, fled to Lower Kamit where she hid herself from Set and his violent army.

15. Anpu and Nebt-Het felt compassion for her and decided to assist her in her misery, and mission to find her husband.

16. Meanwhile in a dream, it was revealed to Auset that the casket found its way to Byblos. A beautiful tree grew around it and encased it in its trunk such that it was hidden. The King of Byblos heard about the tree and cut it down and took it to his palace to serve as a pillar.

17. The following morning Auset set off to Byblos by ship.

18. When she got there, she used her Hekau to impress the Queen of Byblos' servants, thus becoming friends with them. That evening, the servants told their Queen about the beautiful, kind and mysterious black lady from faraway lands. The Queen ordered them to bring Auset to the palace the day after tomorrow. When the Queen met Auset she hired her on the spot and asked her to look after her child. She agreed gladly.

19. One night, the Queen of Byblos found her child surrounded by fire. She screamed and grabbed the child away from it. Unbeknown to her, Auset was conducting a ritual and using Hekau which would have made the child immortal. But by the act of the Queen, she had just broken the power of the ritual, and thus denied him immortality.

20. Auset who had transformed herself into a swallow and had been hovering in sorrow around the pillar quickly turned herself back into a woman. She then told the Queen and King of Byblos everything, who had come into the room after hearing his wife's screams. She asked for the casket and they consented to her taking it back to Kamit. Auset took the casket but left the empty pillar behind.

21. On her voyage back to Kamit, she said a Heka which opened the casket and she hugged her beloved King and husband. The King of Byblos' first son came behind her to secretly watch, but Auset felt his presence and turned around with fire in her eyes. This frightened the boy to death and he fell into the sea.

22. On reaching Kamit, Auset turned herself into a swallow again, and flew around the lifeless body

of the King. She flapped her wings and thus raised the phallus of the King. She then directed the wind from her wings and used it to receive his Divine Seed. The conception of the Divine Child, Heru, came to be, with that act.

23. Auset went to Buto to give birth to the child, "Heru Pa Khrat." This was after she had hidden the body of her husband Ausar in the marshes. However, to her great misfortune Set found the body while he was out hunting for wild boar. He was furious when he saw the casket and recognised it immediately. He opened it, took out the lifeless body of the King, and he butchered it into 14 pieces. He then told his army to scatter the parts all over Kamit.

24. Auset was greatly dismayed when she found out about what Set had done to the body of Ausar. Grieving she went about looking for the body again, with the help of Nebt Het and Anpu. Slowly they found all the thirteen pieces except for the phallus of the lifeless King. This time around, she kept it a secret that she had assembled the different parts of her husband.

25. The land of Kamit was still rife in chaos, as Set's rule continued. Those who had been loyal to Ausar lived in fear as some of them had been either killed or jailed. There were those however who still missed the King and awaited his return, refusing to acknowledge Set's unjust rulership. Every now and then Ausar would appear in a dream to counsel the young "Heru Nej Atef" in how to avenge his father. At other times during the day, Tehuti would also teach the boy and guide him using the Book of Maat.

26. When Heru felt he was ready, he asked Ausar, Auset and Tehuti for permission to go and challenge Set in battle. Before giving him permission Tehuti had one more test for him. He asked the young "Heru Nej Atef" and said, "What is the foremost important law of the spirit to guard against?" Heru responded emphatically, "It is GIGO!" "And what does that mean?" Tehuti asked him again. "It means Garbage In, Garbage Out. If you take in Garbage into your spirit, then you will think, speak and act Garbage in your life." Tehuti was very satisfied with the answers that he received from the young man. And so they gladly allowed him to go and fight, knowing that he would win for he had great teachers and strategic support in them. The battle took place at Edfu and Heru's army was slain ruthlessly in the initial encounter with Set's army.

27. However, Heru's army did not concede. Instead they retreated to re-strategise and fight another day. The following day they went on to attack Set and his army. Even though they were outnumbered, Heru was confident in his family's strategies.

28. The great battle ensued for many days. At one point, Set and Heru faced each other on the battleground. Set succeeded to gash out Heru's eye. Heru then retreated again and went to his camp, but left his regiment in the capable hands of his trusted General, Ba. He asked Tehuti to heal his eye. Tehuti used a Heka and his eye was suddenly healed. It even worked better and with this improved eye he went to fight Set again and managed to castrate him.

29. Losing his manhood caused Set to lose the war. Heru then decided to imprison Set and his men.

Heru had won a decisive victory against Set and his army and the good news quickly spread through Kamit.

30. After the war, Auset, Nebt Het, Anpu and Tehuti went to perform the Open of the Mouth Ceremony for the lifeless King, Ausar.

31. Anpu helped a great deal by mummifying the body of the still of heart.

32. Heru offered his Eye to the King and he was brought back to life.

33. Once he was up, he was pronounced to be the King and Judge of the Dead. His son, Heru, was declared to be King of the Living.

34. Stinking Face, Set, was not pleased with what he was witnessing and protested greatly. He claimed that he was the rightful heir to the throne and Heru had no right to it.

35. The matter was taken to the courts where 42 judges assembled with Tehuti acting as the head of the court. Ausar and Heru were found to have lived by Maat and thus the throne was given to Heru. Set was found guilty of usurping the throne, stealing land from Africans and others, warmongering, and mass genocide over others, amongst many other evil deeds.

36. Punishment was conferred to Set, the Usurper, and he was commanded by the court to protect the Barque of Ausar in the Duat. He was fortunate to not have been killed, contrary to the objective of Heru Neb Taui. But once judgement was given by the court, "Heru Neb Taui" backed off from his preferred objective. The rule of Maat returned to Kamit and the country was once again prosperous, peaceful and well-governed.

Chapter 4

BOOK OF KNOWING THE EVOLUTIONS OF AUSAR AND THE OVERCOMING OF SET

1.   This is the cosmological story of Ausar, Auset and Heru as synthesised by the African scribe, Beloved of Ra, the Creator and the Creation, which are integral and indivisible, and can neither be separated nor divided, and are infinite and eternal, in power and in intelligence.

2.   After Ra came into being out of Nu. He created Shu and Tefnut. Shu and Tefnut gave birth to Nut and Geb, daughter and son.

3.   Geb was the Earth and Nut was the sky. It was said that every night Nut swallowed the sun. Then in the morning, Nut would give birth to it again like a child.

4.   After coming into being, Geb and Nut had their own family consisting of two daughters and two sons. Auset and Nebt Het were their daughters, and Set and Ausar were their sons.

5. Ausar was the first born son of Nut and Geb, followed by Set, Auset and finally Nebt Het. When they grew up, Nebt Het married Set and Auset married Ausar.

6. Ausar was given the earth to rule, the seeds, and fertile soil. He later became the Ruler of the Duat or Amenti, and was known as "Ausar Khenti Amenti".

7. His brother Set was said to have been given the desert and sands, where nothing grows. He became the cause of storms and chaos in the world. He admired the black of the night and was enamoured by sea salt. He was able to change his form to that of an ass, or a hippopotamus, or a crocodile.

8. On the other hand Auset and Nebt Het were very close sisters. One could even mistake them to be one, no different to the other.

9. But they were different in some ways. Auset was the Mut Neter of fertility and nature. She also controls large bodies of water. She discovered the cultivation of grasses into cereals and gave birth to agriculture. Nebt Het finds great pleasure in material things, beauty, music and socialising.

10. It is said that, one day, Nebt Het dressed up as Auset to tempt her own husband Set, into giving her a child. Set who was always busy and focussed on other matters except home, did not take notice of her. However, Ausar unknowingly took Nebt Het thinking she was Auset.

11. Some say though, Nebt Het got Ausar drunk and drew him into her arms, while he was unaware of it. Nebt Het became pregnant and gave birth to Anpu.

12. Set was very jealous of Ausar because he was the King of Kamit. There are those who think that maybe it was because he believed in the rumours that Anpu was not his child.

13. He decided to make an evil plan with 72 conspirators, who were his friends, to kill his brother.

14. Set threw a Royal Feast in honour of Ausar, the King. At the feast there was a beautiful coffin which Set had made with rare imported wood of the best quality and ornaments.

15. Set promised that whoever fit into the coffin perfectly would get to keep it. Nobody, except his 72 friends, knew that he had secretly measured Ausar while he was asleep and made the coffin the exact fit for Ausar.

16. Then everyone lined up to try and fit into the coffin but it would not fit. Some were tall or short. Some were small or big.

17. Finally, it was Ausar's turn to try it. When he tried it, the coffin fit perfectly.

18. Set then slammed it shut and poured molten lead into it. His 72 friends used their powers to subdue everyone at the Royal Feast. No one tried to oppose their plot as they were scared of being killed themselves.

19. Set and his conspirators took the coffin and threw it into the Nile to be swept away.

20. Set then usurped the throne, and became the ruler of Lower and Upper Kamit. Still no one challenged his rule.

21. Isfet, chaos, took over the whole country and Maat, order, was relegated, as it was introduced by Ausar.

22. Auset, the Divine Queen, was heartbroken, and immediately ran away from Kamit with the help of those who loved her husband, Ausar.

23. She set off to find the body of her late husband, the King, Ausar. She sought him untiringly, she wandered round and round about this earth in sorrow, and she alighted not without finding him.

24. Meanwhile, the coffin had been swept onto the shore, in the land of Byblos.

25. A tree grew around the coffin, enclosing it, and concealing it in its trunk.

26. Since the tree was very beautiful it was cut down and used as a pillar for the palace of the King of Byblos.

27. When Auset found out about this, through her working with Heka, she went to the land of Byblos.

28. She found her way to the Royal household and asked to work there and take care of the Royal Child.

29. Auset grew very fond of the child, and one day, she decided to make him immortal. Every night, she would use Heka on the child, and throw him into a fire of Heka to burn away his mortal parts.

30. At times, Auset would then turn herself into a swallow and fly around the pillar weeping for her dead spouse, who was encased in the pillar.

31. One day the Queen of Byblos came home and found her child in the fire of Heka. She was frightened and used water to put the fire out. Auset became angry and revealed to her who she truly was, Auset the runaway Queen of Kamit. She also told her that now her son could never become immortal.

32. She apologized and asked what she could do to help her. Auset asked for the pillar which held Ausar within, and she let her have it, after consulting with the King of Byblos.

33. Auset removed the coffin from the pillar and wept upon it. Then Geb and Nut, unseen and unheard by all including Auset, chimed in, "His wife, Auset, has protected him, and has repulsed the fiends, and turned aside calamities. She uttered the Heka with the magical power of her mouth. Her tongue was perfect, and it never halted at a word. Beneficent in command and word was Auset, the woman of Hekau, the advocate of her husband."

34. Auset then left for Kamit with the coffin. When she got to Kamit, she opened the coffin and turned herself into a bird. She made light with her feathers, she created air with her wings, and she uttered the death wail for her husband. She rose up the inactive members of whose heart was still, she drew from him his essence, and she made an heir to the throne of Kamit for him.

35. She then decided that she would name the Divine Child, Heru, heir to the throne of Kamit, both Upper and Lower Kamit. She then hid the coffin among the marshes. She went away to secretly give birth to the Divine Child. She reared the child in loneliness, at the place where he was not known.

36. One night Set went hunting for wild boar, as this was his favourite sport, he saw the familiar coffin and knew exactly what it was. He was very angry and used Heka to cause a storm to appear. With the power of the storm, he tore the body of Ausar into fourteen pieces. He then used the storm to

scatter the pieces all over Upper and Lower Kamit so no one could find them.

37. Set also heard that the Divine Child, Heru was born, who was the true heir to the throne of Kamit. So he took it upon himself to murder all the new born boys in Kamit to ensure that the child is destroyed before it challenges his rule.

38. When Auset found out about this she became very sad. She immediately went to see if Heru was still safe in hiding. Once she was satisfied that Set could not reach and harm him, she began searching for the fourteen pieces, so that she could put them back together.

39. Nebt Het also helped her, as she felt sorry for her and was angry with Set and was tired of his wicked ways, to say the least.

40. Anpu, Nebt Het's son, also came to help with the search. He had the ability of jackals and was skilful at searching and finding lost possessions.

41. Eventually, the search party found all the missing parts but one, and this was the phallus of the dead King, Ausar. Auset used Heka to make a model of the phallus. Henceforth, they put all the parts together and Ausar looked complete.

42. Auset then performed the Ritual of Life and, with the help of Anpu, she resurrected Ausar back to life.

43. Ausar was then sent to rule the Duat, Amenti, being the first to live there after death. He ruled it as he once ruled the Earth. He was then known as Ausar Khenti Amenti.

44. Again Auset went to the secret place where he was hiding her son to nurture and groom him to

avenge his father and take back the throne. Heru continued to grow up in secrecy.

45. Auset raised the Divine Child and taught him the ways of his African Ancestors, and his late father, the King. She taught him what it means to be African, and what African culture and history entails. Sometimes his uncle Tehuti would tutor the Divine Child. Tehuti taught him many African proverbs and spiritual stories. His favourite proverb which Heru embraced was, "A people without knowledge of their history, culture and spirituality are like a tree without roots." Tehuti told him that the secret to spiritual power is loving yourself, and this is attained through learning about your past heritage as an individual and as a people.

46. Tehuti and Auset also taught Heru that Rituals and Heka are the very essence of African Spirituality (**AS**), History, Culture and Tradition. They warned him that without these aspects, the whole African nation would collapse, regress and revert to Isfet. Moreover, they threatened him that if he, or the nation, forgot their African ways, the Ancestors would curse the very blood that courses through their veins. Heru would not win his battle against Set, and the nation would not prosper as well. His African bloodline would be destined to wandering, lost around the world and be at the bottom of the barrel. Heru took his lessons seriously and never missed any tutorials with his uncle Tehuti and mother, Auset.

47. Ever since they performed the Ritual of Life, Ausar would also appear to give lessons to the little prince. Ausar taught him about ancestral

veneration and showed him how to feed the shrine for the Ancestors. He gave him instruction on warfare as well and shared the mistakes that he made whilst he was on earth. He warned Heru not to repeat these mistakes. He also assured him that since Heru and his mother took care of the ancestral shrine, he would always be there for them. Ausar also instructed him to continue feeding the shrine, providing water, candlelight, incense and regularly cleaning it.

48. Heru grew in strength and stature, and his hand was mighty in the House of Geb. The Paut Neteru rejoiced, and celebrated, at the coming of Heru, the son of Ausar, whose heart was firm, Maa Kheru, the triumphant, the son of Auset, the heir of Ausar.

49. The time came when Ausar felt that Heru was old enough and ready to take on Set, to avenge his father and reclaim the throne. This was after Ausar had tested Heru through several trials and had initiated him in the ways of the African Ancestors. Ausar sat his son down in one of his tutorials, and told him that it was time for him to challenge Set. But he had one more lesson for him.

50. Then Ausar said to his son, "If the eagle comes to the lion and offers it wings, what should it do?" Heru: "I don't know, Atef. But I think it should take them so that it can fly like the eagle." Ausar: "No, Mesu. Think. Think hard and very deeply about this one." Heru: "Hmmm. I still think it should take them. Why should it not take them, Atef?" Ausar: "Because the lion is King, Mesu. It is King of the land. And the eagle is also King. But it is King of the sky. Now, if the lion takes the wings

from the eagle, to fly in the sky, though attractive as they may look, it will no longer be King. Because, Mesu, it will be ruled by the eagle, in the sky." Heru: "Oh, I see, Atef." Ausar: "The Kamityu are only King of the land, Mesu. And if the wizards offer the Kamityu "wings" they should never take them, because they would only be trying to trick the Kamityu." Heru: "Tua Neter! Pa Neter! Neber-Tcher en Pa Neter! Anetch Hrak!"

51. Heru took his army which he had been secretly training with the help of his uncles and marched to the city of Edfu where he challenged Set and his army. The two armies fought for three days and three nights until Heru won convincingly.

52. However, on winning Heru did not kill his uncle Set. Instead it was decided by his mother, Auset and Tehuti that Set would be judged in a Court of Law, with the 42 judges of Maat.

53. Therefore, the day came when Set was taken to court. The 42 judges first listened to Heru's side of the story. After he had finished they then listened to Set and his arguments to what Heru had accused him of.

54. After an 80 year dispute that ensued between Heru and Set, the 42 judges took a decision, and the verdict was given. Set was found guilty of usurping the throne that rightfully belonged to Ausar. But since Ausar was no longer amongst the living, Heru was given the throne of his father. Heru then inherited all privileges, properties and rights that Ausar had whilst he was alive. Set was sentenced to protect the barge of Ra when Ra fought each night with Apep in the Duat.

55. Therefore, peace was restored in the Land of Kamit as Heru made sure that Maat, law and order, was practised again and Isfet, chaos, was abandoned.

56. That is to say, the black people of Kamit received Hetepu, peace and blessings, from the Neteru and the Shepsu, because they lived by Maat, the way of their African Ancestors.

Chapter X

DESTRUCTION OF THE UNIVERSE

1. After his death Ausar finds himself in a cheerless underworld and laments his lot.

2. Ausar: "Oh Atum! What is this desert place into which I have come? It has no water, it has no air, it is depth unfathomable, it is black as the blackest night. I wander helplessly herein. One cannot live here in peace of heart, not may the longings of love be satisfied herein."

3. Atum: "You may live in peace of heart, I have provided illumination in place of water and air, and satisfaction and quiet in the place of bread and beer."

4. Ausar: "But shall I behold your face?"

5. Atum: "I will not allow you to suffer."

6. Ausar: "But every other Neter has his place in the Boat of Millions of Years."

7. Atum: "Your place now belongs to your son Heru."

8. Ausar: "But will he be allowed to dispatch the Great Ones?"

9. Atum: "I have allowed him to dispatch the Great Ones, for he will inherit your throne on the Isle of Fire."

10. Ausar: "How good would it be if one Neter could see another!"

11. Atum: "My face will look upon your face."

12. Ausar: "But how long shall I live?"

13. Atum: "You will live more than millions of years, an era of millions, but in the end I will destroy everything that I have created, the earth will become again part of the Primeval Ocean, like the Abyss of waters in their original state. Then I will be what will remain, just I and Ausar, when I will have changed myself back into the Old Serpent, who knew no man and saw no Neter."

14. Atum: "How fair is that which I have done for Ausar, a fate different from that of all the other Neteru! I have given him the region of the dead while I have put his son Heru as heir upon his throne in the Isle of Fire, I have thus made his place for him in the Boat of Millions of Years, in that Heru remains on his throne to carry on his work."

15. Ausar: "But will not also the soul of Set be sent to the West, a fate different from that of all other Neteru?"

16. Atum: "I shall hold his soul captive in the Boat of Ra, such is my will, so that he will no longer terrorize the Paut Neteru. As above, so below."

BOOK OF AFRICAN SPIRITUALITY

Book of Auset

Chapter 1

ON HIS MAJESTY'S SECRET NAME

1. The logos of the divine and mighty Neter, who created himself, who made the heavens and the earth, and the Breath of Life, and fire, and the Neteru, and men, and beasts, and cattle, and reptiles, and the fowl of the air, and the fish.

2. The Neter who is the king of all men and Neteru, who existed in one form, to whom periods of one hundred and twenty years, are as single years.

3. The Neter whose names by reason of their multitude are unknowable, for even the Neteru know them not.

4. Behold, the Netert Auset lived in the form of a woman, who had the knowledge of Hekau.

5. Her heart turned away in disappointment from the millions of men, and she chose for herself the millions of the Neteru, but esteemed more highly the millions of the spirits.

6. Was it not possible to become even as was Ra in heaven and upon earth, and to make herself mistress of the earth, and a mighty Netert, thus

she meditated in her heart, by the knowledge of the name of the Great Neter.

7.   Behold, Ra entered heaven each day at the head of his mariners, establishing himself upon the double throne of the two horizons.

8.   Now the divine one had become old, he dribbled at the mouth, and he let his emissions go forth from him upon the earth, and his spittle fell upon the ground.

9.   Auset took the spittle and kneaded it in her hand, with some dust, and she fashioned it in the form of a sacred serpent, and made it to have the form of a dart, so that none might be able to escape alive from it.

10.   She left it lying upon the road whereon the Great Neter, Ra, travelled, according to his desire, about the two lands.

11.   Then the Great Neter rose up in the temple of the Neteru in the great double house, among those who were in his train.

12.   As he journeyed on his way according to his daily custom, the serpent shot its fang into him.

13.   The living fire started to depart from the Neter's own body, and the reptile destroyed the dweller among the cedars.

14.   The Mighty Neter opened his mouth, and the cry of His Majesty reached unto the heavens, and the Paut Neteru said, "What is it?" And his Neteru said, "What is the matter?"

15.   And the Great Neter found no words wherewith to answer concerning himself.

16.   His jaws shook, his lips trembled, and the poison took possession of all his flesh just as Hapi takes possession of the land through which he flows.

17. Then the Great Neter made firm his heart and took courage, and cried out to those who were in his following: "Come ye unto me, O ye who have come into being from my members, ye Neteru who have proceeded from me, for I would make you to know what has happened. I have been smitten by some deadly thing, of which my heart has no knowledge, and which I have neither seen with my own eyes nor made with my hand. I have no knowledge at all who has done this to me."

18. "I have never before felt any pain like unto it, and no pain can be worse than this pain. I am a Prince, the son of a Prince, and the divine emanation which was produced from a Neter. I am a Great One, the son of a Great One, and my father has determined for me my name. I have multitudes of names, and I have multitudes of forms, and my being exists in every Neter. I have been invoked by Temu and Heru-Hekennu."

19. "My father and my mother uttered my name, and they hid it in my body at my birth, so that no one would use Hekau against me and succeed. It was done so that none would make enchantments and have dominion over me."

20. "I had come forth from my temple to look upon that which I had made, and was making my way through the two lands which I had made, when a blow was aimed at me, but I know not of what kind."

21. "Behold, is it fire? Behold, is it water? My heart is full of burning fire, my limbs ache, shivering, and my members have darting pains in them. Let there be brought unto me, my children the Neteru, who possess Hekau, whose mouths are

skilled in uttering them, and whose powers reach up to heaven."

22. Then his children came unto him, and every Neter was there with his cry of lamentation.

23. Auset came with her Hekau, and the place of her mouth was filled with the Breath of Life, for the words which she puts together destroy diseases, and her words make to live those whose throats are.

24. And she said, "What is this, O divine father? What is it? Has a serpent shot his venom into thee? Has a thing which thou hast fashioned lifted up its head against thee? Verily it shall be overthrown by beneficent Hekau, words of power, and I will make it to retreat in the sight of thy rays."

25. The Mighty Neter opened his mouth, saying: "I was going along the road and passing through the two lands of my country, for my heart desired to look upon what I had made, when I was bitten by a serpent which I did not see. Behold, is it fire? Behold, is it water? I am colder than water. I am hotter than fire. All my members sweat. I myself quake, my eye is unsteady. I cannot look at the heavens. Water forces itself on my face as in the time of the inundation."

26. And Auset said unto Ra, "O my divine father, tell me thy name, for he who is able to pronounce his name lives."

27. Ra said, "I am the maker of the heavens and the earth, I have knit together the mountains, and I have created everything which exists upon them. I am the maker of the Waters, and I have made Meht-Ur to come into being, I have made the

Bull of his Mother, and I have made the joys of love to exist."

28. "I am the maker of heaven, and I have made to be hidden the two Neteru of the horizon, and I have placed the souls of the Neteru within them. I am the Being who opens his eyes and the light comes."

29. "I am the Being who shuts his eyes and there is darkness. I am the Being who gives the command, and the waters of Hapi burst forth."

30. "I am the Being whose name the Neteru do not know. I am the maker of the hours and the creator of the days. I am the opener of the festivals, and the maker of the floods of water. I am the creator of the Fire of Life whereby the works of the houses are caused to come into being."

31. "I am Kheperi in the morning, Ra at the time of his culmination, and Temu in the evening."

32. Nevertheless the poison was not driven from its course, and the Great Neter felt no better.

33. Then Auset said unto Ra, "Among the things which you have said unto me, thy name has not been mentioned. O declare it unto me, and the poison shall come forth, for the person who has declared his name shall live."

34. Meanwhile the poison burned with blazing fire and the heat thereof was stronger than that of a blazing flame.

35. Then the Majesty of Ra, said, "I will allow myself to be searched through by Auset, and my name shall come forth from my body and go into hers."

36. Then the divine one hid himself from the Neteru, and the throne in the "Boat of Millions of Years" was empty.

37. And it came to pass that when it was the time for the heart to come forth from the Neter, she said unto her son Heru, "The Great Neter shall bind himself by an oath to give his two eyes."

38. Thus was the Great Neter made to yield up his name, and Auset, the great Lady of Hekau, said, "Flow on, poison, and come forth from Ra, let the Eye of Heru come forth from the Neter and shine, outside his mouth. I have worked, and I make the poison to fall on the ground, for the venom has been mastered. Verily the name hath been taken away from the Great Neter."

39. "Let Ra live, and let the poison die, and if the poison live then Ra shall die. And similarly, a certain man, the son of a certain man, shall live and the poison shall die."

40. These were the words which Auset spoke, the great Lady of Hekau, the mistress of the Neteru, and she had knowledge of Ra, "In His own Name."

41. The above words shall be said over an image of Temu and an image of Heru-Hekennu, and over an image of Auset and an image of Heru.

Chapter 2

SEVEN SCORPIONS

1.   Anuk Auset, Mut Neter, Nebt Tep Ihet, Ur Nebt Hekau. I am Auset, Mother Nature, Lady of the Cow's Head, Great Lady of Words of Power.

2.   I have come from the secret place, wherein my brother Set had put me. Tehuti, the great Neter, the lord of the truth in heaven and on earth, had said to me: "Do come, Auset divine, it is well to listen, conceal yourself with your young son, that he may return to us, when his body is strong and his strength has completely developed and you make him sit down on his father's throne and the office of the lord of the two lands is granted to him."

3.   I went out in the evening-hour and seven scorpions went out behind me. They led me: Tefen and Befen close behind me, Mestet and Mestetef under my stretcher, Petet, Tetet and Maatet prepared my way.

4.   I ordered them emphatically and my words penetrated into their ears: "Do not know 'the black one' and do not greet 'the red one,' do not distinguish 'the high one' from 'the humble one,' be your face turned downwards to the road, be

careful not to lead him who looks for me, until we have reached 'The House of the Crocodile,' the beginning of the Delta Marshes, the marshes of Db."

5.	Finally, I reached the houses of matrons. As soon as a noble lady had seen me from afar, she closed her door to me.

6.	This annoyed my seven companions. They deliberated on it and put their poison together on the sting of Tefen.

7.	A fisher-girl opened her door for me and we entered the shabby dwelling. But Tefen had penetrated under the door and she stung the lady's son. Because she had not opened to me, her heart was sad and she did not know whether he was alive. She wandered about her town lamenting, but nobody came to her voice.

8.	My heart, for that reason, was uneasy about the child that I wished to cure the innocent one. I called to her, saying, "Come to me, come to me, behold my mouth bears life. I am a daughter known in her town, who expels the poisonous snake with her spell. My father has taught me knowledge. I am his beloved daughter."

9.	Auset laid her hands on the child to cure him who was short of breath: "Poison of Tefen, come, go out to the earth, do not go about and do not penetrate. Poison of Befen, come, go out to the earth, I am Auset, divine mistress of Hekau, exercising Heka, magical in speaking, effective of words. Every biting snake obeys me. Fall down, poison of Mestet, do not run. Poison of Mestetef, do not rise, I command you poison of Petet and Tetet. Fall down, mouth of the biting one, at the words of Auset divine, Great of Hekau among the Neteru, to whom Geb has given his Hekau power in order to avert the poison in its power. Yield, recede, flee, backwards, poison, do not jump up, at the words of the beloved of Ra, the egg of the smn-bird and who has come forth from the sycamore."

10. The lady came and brought her possessions, and filled the house of the fisher-girl on behalf of the fisher-girl, who had opened her stable to me, but the lady had been worried during one night and had tasted the effects of her utterance, for her son had been bitten and she had brought her possessions because she had not opened to me.

11. May the child live and the poison die. Then Heru will be healthy for his mother Auset, and the patient will be healthy for his mother likewise. Bread of barley drives out the poison, it flees on account of hmn.

12. This Hekau is spoken over bread of barley mixed with salt, to take and to bind on it.

13. Auset then continued her journey and came to Khemmis in the Delta, where she gave birth to Heru, "Heru-Avenger-Of-His-Father."

Chapter 3

THE GREEN JEWEL

1.   Prince Khafra stood before His Majesty, and said: "I will relate a marvel which happened in the days of the Nesu, Sneferu, thy father."

2.   Then he told the story of the green jewel.

3.   One day, Sneferu was disconsolate and weary.

4.   He wandered about the palace with desire to be cheered.

5.   But he found nothing to take the gloom from his mind.

6.   He requested his chief scribe to be brought before him, and said: "I would like to have entertainment, but cannot find any in this place."

7.   The scribe said: "Thy Majesty should go boating on the lake, and let the rowers be the prettiest girls in your harem. It will delight your heart to see them splashing the water where the birds dive and to gaze upon the green shores and the flowers and trees. I myself will go with you."

8.   The Nesu consented, and twenty virgins who were black and beautiful to behold went into the boat, and they rowed with oars of ebony which were decorated with gold.

9.   His Majesty took pleasure in the outing, and the gloom passed from his heart as the boat went hither and thither, and the girls sang together with sweet voices.

10.   It so happened, as they were turning round, an oar handle brushed against the hair of the girl who was steering, and shook from it a green jewel, which fell into the water.

11.   She lifted up her oar and stopped singing, and the others grew silent and ceased rowing.

12.   Said Sneferu: "Do not pause, let us go on still farther."

13.   The girls said: "She who steers has lifted her oar."

14.   Said Sneferu to her: "Why have you lifted your oar?"

15.   "Alas, I have lost my green jewel. It has fallen into the lake," she said.

16.   Sneferu said: "I will give you another, let us go on."

17.   The girl pouted and answered back: "I would rather have my own green jewel again than any other."

18.   His Majesty said to the chief scribe: "I am given great enjoyment by this novelty. Indeed my mind is much refreshed, as the beautiful girls row me up and down the lake. Now one of them has lost her green jewel, which has dropped into the water, and she wants it back again and will not have another to replace it."

19.   The chief scribe at once muttered a Heka.

20.   Then by reason of his magic words the waters of the lake were divided like a lane.

21.   He went down and found the green jewel which the girl had lost, and came back with it to her.

22. When he did that, he again uttered more Hekau, and the waters came together as they were before.
23. The Nesu was very pleased, and when he had full enjoyment with the rowing upon the lake, he returned to the palace.
24. He gave gifts to the chief scribe, and everyone wondered at the marvel which he had accomplished.
25. Such was Prince Khafra's tale of the green jewel, and King Khufu commanded that offerings should be laid in the tombs of Sneferu and his chief scribe, who was a great magician.
26. Next Prince Hordedef stood before the king, and he said: "Your Majesty has heard tales regarding the wonders performed by magicians in other days, but I can bring forth a worker of marvels who now lives in the kingdom."
27. King Khufu said: "And who is he, my son?"

Chapter 4

DJEDI MASTER
OF HEKAU

1. "His name is Djedi," answered Prince Hordedef.
    "He is a very old man, for his years are a hundred
    and ten. Each day he eats a joint of beef and five
    hundred loaves of bread, and drinks a hundred
    jugs of beer. He can smite off the head of a
    living creature and restore it again. He can make
    a lion follow him, and he knows the secrets of
    the habitation of the Neter Tehuti, which Your
    Majesty has desired to know so that you may
    design the chambers of your pyramid."

2. King Khufu said: "Go now and find this man for
    me, Hordedef."

3. The prince went down to the Nile, boarded a boat,
    and sailed southward until he reached the town
    called Dedsnefru, where Djedi had his dwelling.

4. He went ashore, and was carried in his chair of
    state towards the magician, who was found lying
    at his door.

5. When Djedi was awakened, the king's son saluted
    him and bade him not to rise up because of his
    years.

6. The prince said: "My royal father desires to honour you, and will provide for you a tomb among your people."

7. Djedi blessed the prince and the king with thankfulness, and he said to Hordedef: "Greatness be thine, may your Ka have victory over the powers of evil, and may your Khu follow the path which leads to Paradise."

8. Hordedef assisted Djedi to rise up, and took his arm to help him towards the ship.

9. He sailed away with the prince, and in another ship were his assistants and his magic books.

10. "Aankh, Udja, Seneb, Health, Prosperity and Wellness, and plenty be thine," said Hordedef, when he again stood before his royal father King Khufu. "I have come down stream with Djedi, the great magician."

11. His Majesty was very pleased, and said: "Let the man be brought into my presence."

12. Djedi came and saluted the Nesu, who said: "Why have I not seen you before?"

13. "He that is called cometh," answered the old man, "you have sent for me and I am here."

14. "It is told," King Khufu said, "that you can restore the head that is taken from a live creature."

15. "I can indeed, Your Majesty," answered Djedi.

16. The king said: "Then let a prisoner be brought forth and decapitated."

17. "I would rather it were not a man," said Djedi, "I do not deal even with cattle in such a manner."

18. A duck was brought forth and its head was cut off, and the head was thrown to the right and the body to the left.

19. Djedi spoke Hekau. Then the head and the body came together, and the duck rose up and quacked loudly.

20. The same was done with a goose.

21. King Khufu then requested a cow to be brought in, and its head was cut off.

22. Djedi restored the animal to life again, and made it to follow him.

23. His Majesty then spoke to the magician and said: "It is told that you possess the secrets of the dwelling of the Neter Tehuti."

24. Djedi answered: "I do not possess them, but I know where they are concealed, and that is within a temple chamber at Heliopolis. There the plans are kept in a box, but it is no ordinary person who shall bring them to Your Majesty."

25. "I would like to know who will deliver them unto me," King Khufu said.

26. Djedi prophesied that three sons would be born to Rud-dedit, wife of the chief priest of Ra.

27. The eldest would become chief priest at Heliopolis and would possess the plans.

28. He and his brothers would one day sit upon the throne and rule over all the land.

29. King Khufu's heart was filled with gloom and alarm when he heard the prophetic words of the great magician.

30. Djedi then said: "What are your thoughts, O King? Behold your son will reign after you, and then his son. But thereafter, one of these children will follow."

31. King Khufu was silent. Then he spoke and asked: "When will these three children be born?"

32. Djedi informed His Majesty, who then said: "I will visit the temple of Ra at that time."
33. Djedi was honoured by His Majesty, and thereafter dwelt in the house of the Prince Hordedef.
34. He was given daily his portion an ox, a thousand loaves of bread, a hundred jugs of beer, and a hundred bunches of onions.

Chapter 5

SONS OF RA

1.   When the day drew nigh in which the three sons were to be born, Ra ordered the four Netertu, Auset, Nebt-Het, Meskhenet, and Heqet, and the Neter Khnum, to go and supervise the birth of the three children.

2.   It was done so that when they grew up, and ruled throughout all Kamit, they would build temples to them, and furnish the altars with offerings of meat and drink in abundance.

3.   Auset and Nebt-Het were the daughters of Nut and Geb, and sisters of Ausar and Set. Auset was the mother of Heru, and Nebt-Het was the mother of Anpu.

4.   Heqet was a Frog-Netert, who was associated with generation and birth. Meskhenet was a Neter who assisted at the creation of the world, and who fashioned the bodies of men and women.

5.   Then the four Netertu changed themselves into the forms of dancing women, and went to the house wherein the lady Rud-dedit lay ill, and finding her husband, the priest of Ra, who was called Ra-User, outside, they clashed their cymbals

together, and rattled their sistra, and tried to make him merry.

6.   When Ra-User objected to this and told them that his wife lay ill inside the house, they replied, "Let us see her, for we know how to help her." So he said to them and to Khnum who was with them, "Come in," and they did so, and they went to the room wherein Rud-dedit lay.

7.   Auset, Nebt-Het, and Heqet assisted in bringing the three boys into the world. Meskhenet prophesied for each of them sovereignty over the land, and Khnum bestowed health upon their bodies.

8.   After the birth of the three boys, the four Netertu and Khnum went outside the house, and told Ra-User to rejoice because his wife Ruddedit had given him three children.

9.   Ra-User said, "My Ladies, what can I do for you in return for this?"

10.   Having apparently nothing else to give them, he begged them to have barley brought from his granary, so that they might take it away as a gift to their own granaries.

11.   They agreed, and the Neter Khnum brought the barley.

12.   So the Netertu set out to go to the place whence they had come.

13.   When they had arrived there Auset said to her companions: "How is it that we who went to Rud-dedit, by the command of Ra, have worked no wonder for the children which we could have announced to their father, who allowed us to depart without begging a boon?"

14. So they made divine crowns such as belonged to the King, life, strength, health be to him, and they hid them in the barley.

15. Then they sent rain and storm through the heavens, and they went back to the house of Ra-User, carrying the barley with them, and said to him, "Let the barley abide in a sealed room until we dance our way back to the north."

16. So they put the barley in a sealed room.

17. After Rud-dedit had kept herself secluded for fourteen days, she said to one of her handmaidens, "Is the house all ready?"

18. And the handmaiden told her that it was provided with everything except jars of barley drink, which had not been brought.

19. Rud-dedit then asked why they had not been brought, and the handmaiden replied in words that seem to mean that there was no barley in the house except that which belonged to the dancing Netertu, and that it was in a chamber which had been sealed with their seal.

20. Rud-dedit then told her to go and fetch some of the barley, for she was quite certain that when her husband Ra-User returned he would make good what she took.

21. Thereupon the handmaiden went to the chamber, and broke it open. She heard in it, loud cries and shouts, and the sounds of music and singing and dancing.

22. She also heard all the noises which men make in honour of the birth of a King.

23. She went back and told Rud-dedit what she had heard.

24. Then Rud-dedit herself went through the room, and could not find the place where the noises came from.

25. But when she laid her head against the box, she realised that the noises were inside it.

26. She then took this box, which cannot have been of any great size, and put it in another box, which in turn she put in another box, which she sealed, and then wrapped this in a leather covering.

27. She laid it in a chamber containing her jar of barley beer, and sealed the door.

28. When Ra-User returned from the fields, Ruddedit related to him everything that had happened, and his heart was very joyful, and he and his wife sat down and enjoyed themselves.

29. A few days after these events Rud-dedit had a quarrel with her handmaiden, and she slapped her hard.

30. The handmaiden was very angry, and in the presence of the household she said words to this effect: "Does thou dare to treat me in this way? I who can destroy thee? She has given birth to three kings, and I will go and tell His Majesty King Khufu of this fact."

31. The handmaiden thought that, if Khufu knew of the views of Ra-User and Rud-dedit about the future of their three sons, and the prophecies of the Netertu, he would kill the children and perhaps their parents also.

32. With the objective in her mind of telling the king, the handmaiden went to her maternal uncle, whom she found weaving flax on the walk, and told him what had happened.

33. She said she was going to tell the king about the three children.

34. From her uncle she obtained neither support nor sympathy. On the contrary, gathering together several strands of flax into a thick rope he gave her a good beating.

35. A little later the handmaiden went to the river to fetch some water, and whilst she was filling her pot, a crocodile seized her and carried her away and ate her.

36. Then the uncle went to the house of Ruddedit to tell her what had happened, and he found her sitting down, with her head bowed over her breast, and extremely sad and miserable.

37. He asked her, saying, "O Lady, wherefore art thou so sad?"

38. And she told him that the cause of her sorrow was the handmaiden, who had been born in the house and had grown up in it. The same one who had just left it, threatening that she would go and tell the king about the birth of the three kings.

39. The uncle of the handmaiden nodded his head in a consoling manner, and told Rud-dedit how she had come to him and informed him what she was going to do. He told her that he gave her a good beating with a rope of flax, and that she went to a river to fetch some water, afterwards. However, a crocodile carried her off.

40. Rud-dedit was very pleased with what she heard such that she gave the uncle of the handmaiden some food and gifts. When her husband came back she broke the good news to him and they both celebrated their good blessings.

Chapter 6

KARA RECITES
A HYMN TO AUSET

1. On a beautiful Monday morning, during the hour of Auset, a wise young beautiful black woman from Kamit, prepares herself to make offerings to the shrine of Auset. After making offerings to her shrine dedicated to the Great Netert, Auset, she recites a hymn to Auset, and she says with a melodic voice:

2. "Praise to you Auset the Great Divine Mother, Lady of Heaven, Mistress, Woman of the Neteru.

3. You are the Head royal wife of Un Nefer. The supreme overseer of the golden ones in the temple. The eldest son, first born of Geb.

4. You are the head royal wife of Un Nefer. The Bull, Lion who overthrows all his enemies. Lord and Ruler for Eternity.

5. You are the first chosen of Un Nefer. Beautiful Youth who hacks up the Rebels in the Two Lands.

6. You are the Head Royal Wife of Un Nefer. Protector of Her Brother, and sets apart and makes sacred the weary hearted.

7. You are the Head Royal Wife of Un Nefer. Eternal Youth, Holding up Eternity.
8. You are with him in Senmut, the Place where he is buried."

Chapter 7

DEATH AND RESURRECTION OF HERU

1. I am Auset. I conceived a child, Heru, and I brought him forth in a cluster of papyrus plants. I rejoiced exceedingly, for in him I saw one who would make answer for his father.

2. I hid him, and I covered him up carefully, being afraid of that foul one, Set, and then I went to the town of Am, where the people gave thanks for me because they knew I could cause them trouble.

3. I passed the day in collecting food for the child, and when I returned and took Heru into my arms, I found him, Heru, the beautiful one of gold, the boy, the child, lifeless!

4. He had bedewed the ground with the water of his eye and with the foam of his lips.

5. His body was motionless, his heart did not beat, and his muscles were relaxed.

6. Then I sent forth a bitter cry, and lamented loudly my misfortune, for now that my son, Heru, the Golden One, was dead I had none to protect me, or to take vengeance on Set.

7. When the people heard my voice they went out to me, and they bewailed with me the greatness of my affliction.

8. But although all lamented on my behalf there was none who could bring back Heru to life.

9. Then a woman who was well known in her town, a lady who was the mistress of property in her own right, went out to me, and consoled me, and assured me that the child should live through his mother.

10. And she said, "A scorpion has stung him, the reptile has wounded him."

11. Then I bent my face over the child, and I examined the wound, and found that there was poison in it, and then taking him in my arms, I leaped about with him like a fish that is put upon hot coals, uttering loud cries of lamentation.

12. During this outburst of grief the Netert Nebt-Het, my sister, arrived, and she too lamented and cried bitterly over my loss, with her came the Scorpion-Netert Serket.

13. Nebt-Het at once advised me to cry out for help to Ra, the Father of the Neteru, for it is impossible for the Boat of Ra to travel across the sky whilst Heru, the Divine Child, is lying dead.

14. Then I cried out, and made supplication to the "Boat of Millions of Years," and Ra heard me and stopped the Boat.

15. Out of it came down Tehuti, who was provided with powerful Hekau, and, coming to me, he inquired concerning my troubles. "What is it, what is it, O Auset, thou Netert of Hekau, whose mouth has skill to utter them with supreme effect. Surely no evil thing has befallen Heru, for the

Boat of Ra has him under its protection. I have come from the Boat of Ra to heal Heru."

16. Then Tehuti told me not to fear, but to put away all anxiety from my heart, for he had come to heal the Divine Child, and he told me that Heru was fully protected because he was the dweller in his disk, the firstborn son of heaven, the Great Dwarf, the Mighty Ram, the Great Hawk, the Sacred Beetle, the Hidden Body, the Governor of the Duat, the Sacred Benu Bird. He was also protected by the Hekau of Auset, the names of Ausar, the weeping of his mother and brethren, and by his own name and heart.

17. Turning towards the child, Tehuti began to recite his Hekau and said, "Wake up, Heru! Thy protection is established. Make thou happy the heart of thy mother Auset. The words of Heru bind up hearts and he comforts him that is in affliction. Let your hearts rejoice, O ye dwellers in the heavens. Heru who avenges his father shall make the poison to retreat. That which is in the mouth of Ra shall circulate, and the tongue of the Great Neter shall overcome opposition. The Boat of Ra stands still and moves not, and the Sun is in the place where it was yesterday to heal Heru for his mother Auset. Come to earth, draw nigh, O Boat of Ra. O ye Mariners of Ra make the boat to move and convey food of the town of Sekhem hither, to heal Heru for his mother Auset. Come to earth, O poison! I am Tehuti the firstborn son, the son of Ra. Tern and the Paut Neteru have commanded me to heal Heru for his mother Auset. O Heru, O Heru, thy Ka protects thee, and thy Image works protection for thee.

The poison is as the daughter of its own flame. It is destroyed because it smote the strong son. Your temples are safe, for Heru lives for his mother."

18. Three days later, the Divine Child, Heru returned to life, to the joy of my heart as a mother.

19. Tehuti went back to the "Boat of Millions of Years," which at once proceeded on its majestic course, and all the Neteru from one end of heaven to the other rejoiced.

20. I requested in earnest Ra and Tehuti that Heru might be nursed and brought up by the Neteru of the town of Buto, in the Delta.

21. Then at once Tehuti committed the child to their care, and instructed them about his future.

22. Heru grew up in Buto under their protection. When he became of age he built an army that would take on the army of Set.

23. While he assembled his army there were those who would come and mock him daily for building such an army. They thought that he was crazy to even think that he would challenge the mighty Set.

24. They would go to where he was training and drink beer and wine and ridicule the young Heru. They would taunt him and call him all sorts of names such as "Bastard Child" because they did not know who his father was.

25. Moreover these tormenters did not know that his mother was actually the Queen Auset, because she had used Hekau to disguise herself.

26. Heru would just ignore them and he told his growing army to do the same. He told them that his smart actions, and their victory against Set,

would do the talking, not debating with fools. He was convinced that it was the wiser route to take.

27.   In due course, the time came when he took his large army of brave men and women to Edfu and fought a great battle with Set.

28.   Heru vanquished Set and his army, and so avenged the wrong done to his father, Ausar, by Set.

Chapter 8

FESTIVAL SONGS OF
AUSET AND NEBT-HET

1. It was during the great festival of Ausar, which took place in the fourth month of the Season of Akhet and lasted five days.

2. Two young beautiful black women who were virgins wore fillets of sheep's wool on their heads, and held tambourines in their hands.

3. One was called Auset and the other Nebt-Het.

4. Both young women sang the songs of Auset and Nebt Het, in front of the crowd that had gathered.

5. Come, come, run to me, O strong heart! Let me see thy divine face, for I do not see thee, and make thou clear the path that we may see thee as we see Ra in heaven, when the heavens unite with the earth, and cause darkness to fall upon the earth each day.

6. My heart burns with fire at thy escape from the Fiend, even as my heart burns with fire, when thou turns thy side to me.

7. O that thou wouldst never remove it from me!

8. O thou who unites the Two Domains, and who turns back those who are on the roads, I seek to see thee because of my love for thee.

9. Thou flies like a living being, O Everlasting King, thou hast destroyed the fiend Anrekh.

10. Thou art the King of the South and of the North, and thou goes forth from Tatchesert.

11. May there never be a moment in thy life when I do not fill thy heart, O my divine brother, my lord who goes forth from Aqert.

12. My arms are raised to protect thee, O thou whom I love.

13. I love thee, O Husband, Brother, Lord of Love, come thou in peace into thy house.

14. Thy hair is like turquoise as thou comes forth from the Fields of Turquoise, thy hair is like unto the finest lapis-lazuli, and thou thyself art more blue than thy hair.

15. Thy skin and body are like southern alabaster, and thy bones are of silver.

16. The perfume of thy hair is like new myrrh, and thy skull is of lapis-lazuli.

Chapter 9

MATTERS OF THE AB

1. Sameri and Rayiti were going through marital issues that required serious attention. As twins, of different sexes, they relied primarily on each other for companionship and advice on relationship problems. "Matters of the Ab," as they used to affectionately refer to such issues.

2. This time around, Sameri, the male twin, wanted to marry a beautiful black woman that he had been smitten with from Annu. The problem was that he was already married to another black beauty, Abti. And now he was faced with the challenge of telling Abti that he wanted to take a second wife.

3. Even though it was customary in Kamit for him to take another wife if he so wished to, it was not an easy process. To initiate the exercise, he had to get permission from the first wife, and then ask the Elders to be qualified to assess whether he was fit for purpose.

4. It involved the elders making sure that Sameri had enough surplus resources to maintain a second family. Not just anyone could take a second or even a third wife. You had to prove that you had the resources to sustain multiple families.

Essentially, you had to prove that you were "man enough" as it were.

5. There were three laws that had to be obeyed, which were codified in the well-known and ancient "Book of Nebt Het."

6. The first law required that the main house be respected, loved and cherished, always.

7. The second law demanded that the first house should not be replaced by the second house, as they served different purposes.

8. And lastly, the third law stipulated that the man must have enough resources to gratify all the houses.

9. It was easy for the Nesu and the Nobles to have multiple wives because they could effortlessly meet the third law, without fail.

10. These laws were created to maintain and secure Maat in the family and community.

11. In Sameri's case, that was not a problem for he had plenty resources. The issue was asking his wife for permission. That unsettled his nerves tremendously.

12. He had told his wife, the first time they met, that he would never want another woman. But this was no longer the case for him. Because he had met Khatu, and on that very day he saw her, his world changed.

13. Khatu was no ordinary woman.

14. She was very beautiful, smart, inquisitive and humble. She was full of life and zest, and had a good heart. Khatu was simply the "flower of the community," an African expression that meant she was extremely attractive, out of the ordinary.

15. Her looks were spellbinding and her heart was inspiring. All men desired her, and for some reason she had fallen for Sameri, and they just wanted to be together, they could not imagine a life without each other.

16. And Khatu did not care that he was already married. In fact, being a second wife was okay with her, she had grown up in a plural family anyway, and she knew how to manoeuvre her way in such an arrangement.

17. She was truly African, in heart and mind, and respected the Ways of the Ancestors.

18. She appreciated the fact that Africans were an Ancient race of people. They were the only people on earth to have observed, experienced and clocked several precessions, and so she trusted her African Ancestors' Wisdom. It was unparalleled and unmatched by any other people.

19. They had also proven themselves because Kamit and many other African nations lasted for a long time, several millennia, as stable and overall peaceful nations. The Way of Maat ruled in Africa.

20. On the other hand, Sameri's sister, Rayiti, was going through a different experience, but still challenging to say the least. Her issue was that she wanted out of her marriage.

21. She wanted to divorce her husband, Behudet. He was a violent man who ill-treated her, any chance that he got.

22. It was especially true when he came back home drunk from spending time with his wayward friends. She had decided it was time for her to leave him.

23. Rayiti had spoken to her parents and Behudet's parents to ask for permission and argue her case.
24. They understood her position and had pleaded with Behudet on numerous times, to try and rehabilitate him, but his behaviour never improved.
25. Although it was hard, both families agreed that the relationship was irreconcilable, for violence against women was not tolerated in African culture. It was shunned upon.
26. Women were considered equals, in many ways. In authentic and untainted African Culture, there was no nonsense against women, for African men adored their mothers, sisters and daughters, and treated them like the Neterut that they represented in this realm.
27. Powerful Black Queens such as Hatshepsut, Ahmes, Nefertari and many others were an inspiration to many African women.
28. The peaceful, harmonious and natural relationship between men and women in Africa was codified in Maat.
29. And no sane and healthy African man dared to go against the Way of Maat. To do so, would have been the same as declaring war against your own Ba and Ka.
30. Rayiti had already filed her intention with the courts in Kamit, and she knew that she was not going to face any complications.
31. Fortunately, before the marriage ceremony, Rayiti and Behudet had signed an agreement which secured her rights, her children's future, and guaranteed her an allowance.

32. Moreover, the agreement also stated that any material goods she brought into the marriage would be hers to keep even after the divorce. She and her husband could also own land separate from each other.

33. In Kamit, divorce was a simple procedure where she had to draft a statement in front of the courts and witnesses, declaring that the marriage was being annulled.

34. Rayiti was going to get custody of the two children that they had, as per the norm, moreover she was free to remarry afterwards.

35. That night when she met with her brother, Sameri, she had brought along with her the original document that represented her marriage to Behudet. It was of sentimental value to her but she knew she had to let it go.

36. The document contained many legal details: the date of their marriage, Behudet's signature and hers, their parents' names, Behudet's profession, the scribe who drew up the contract, names of the witnesses and the details of the settlement.

37. All of this was now going to waste, she thought to herself. She had gotten hold of the agreement from the local Temple where all the marriage contracts were stored.

38. They let her have it because they knew that she was in the process of an annulment.

39. Sameri and Rayiti looked at each other and shook their heads. Sameri was first to speak: "Hetepu, senet!"

40. Rayiti: "Hetepu, sene!"

41. Sameri: "Nej Kheret? How are you feeling about everything that has happened?"

42. Rayiti: "I never thought that it would come to this ... or that it would be this hard. I gave it my all ... to try and make it work for me and my children. Tu, Behudet was very violent with me. As they say, 'There's worms in men's spirits,' but Behudet never cared to cleanse himself. However, I still care for him dearly ... and it is hard for me to go through with this. He is the father of my two children after all."

43. Sameri: "I understand. These things are never easy. But as always, I am here for you if you need anything."

44. Rayiti: "I know sene, I know. How is it going with you? Nej Kheret?"

45. Sameri: "Nejem. Thank you for asking. I've made my decision. I will go ahead with the second marriage. I love Khatu, and Abti will just have to understand. It is the African way and I am exercising my rights. I can afford to take good care of another family, or even three, for that matter."

46. Rayiti: "I thought you love Abti, and only her, isn't that what you promised her when you first met her."

47. Sameri: "Tu, it's true. I love her dearly. But I also love Khatu, and she loves me. I am of the conviction that you can love as many people as you so desire. As long as a woman is beautiful according to your personal definition, and shares the same Values, Interests and Principles, then why not? Remember, it is our understanding, as Africans, that the Ancestors want us to have as many children as permissible. In this way, they can come back and reincarnate. They can 'wehem aankh.' By having many children, we give

them that opportunity. We make available the bodies that they can inhabit. Abti can no longer have any more children. She claims her body is tired now, after six children. I understand her position. However, I have so much Shekhem in me, and thus want to have more children. I am a responsible person Rayiti. It is not just unruly lust that's motivating me."

48. Rayiti: "I understand you sene, but I, myself, would never share my husband with anyone. I know and understand that it's our Way of Life. But that's just my stance, and I would have been willing to stay unmarried if it had come to that. I'm glad I have two healthy and beautiful children to show from this failed marriage. It pleases me very much."

49. Sameri: "I'm happy for you senet. It will all go well, for both of us. The Shepsu and Neteru are with us, everywhere we go. At first, Abti will be reluctant but as time goes, I know her heart will soften. She will learn to accept Khatu. For Khatu is very respectful, and Abti is also very accommodating. That's just her spirit. And so it is decided. As it is willed and so shall it be."

50. Rayiti: "It is true what you say. Do you need my help?"

51. Sameri: "Tern. I think it is better I take care of everything myself. It's my bed and I'm going to sleep on it. So it's best I go through the motions on my own. And you?"

52. Rayiti: "Tua U for asking, I too have everything I need. I have a solid plan laid out. But I'll take you up on the offer should anything difficult come up."

53. Sameri: "In that case, take good care senet. I will see you next time. I just wanted to talk to you very briefly and update you with the latest on my side. Aankh Udja Seneb!"
54. Rayiti: "Anytime, anytime. Senebty, sene!"
55. Sameri: "Tua Neter. Tua Shepsu."

BOOK OF AFRICAN SPIRITUALITY

Book of Heru

Chapter 1

AN ABOMINABLE PIG

1. O you of the evening, you swamp-dwellers, you of Mendes, you of Buto, you of the shade of Ra which knows not praise, you who brew stoppered beer. Do you know why Rekhyt, Lower Kamit, was given to Heru?

2. It was Ra who gave it to him in recompense for the injury in his eye.

3. It was Ra, he said to Heru, "Let me see your eye since this has happened to it." It was injured in the fight with Set.

4. Then Ra saw it. Ra said, "Look at that injury in your eye, while your hand is covering over the good eye which is there."

5. Then Heru looked at that injury. It assumed the form of a black pig. Thereupon Heru shrieked because of the state of his eye, which was stormy and inflamed.

6. Heru said, "Behold, my eye is as at that first blow which Set made against my eye!" Thereupon, Heru swallowed his heart before him and lost consciousness.

7. Then Ra said: "Put him upon his bed until he has recovered." It was Set, he has assumed another

form against him, as a black pig, thereupon he shot a blow into his eye.

8. Then Ra said: "The pig is an abomination to Heru." "With that he might be able to recover," said the Neteru. That is how the pig became an abomination to the Neteru, as well as men, for Heru's sake.

Chapter 2

80 YEARS OF CONTENTION BETWEEN HERU AND SET

1. Heru, the avenger of his father, Ausar, came before the Great Paut Neteru. With his mother, Queen Auset, beside him, he spoke of the cruel murder of his father at the hands of Set. He spoke of the usurpation of the throne of Kamit. The Neteru were impressed by the eloquence of the falcon-headed one, and they pitied him.

2. Shu, son of the creator, was the first to speak, "Right should rule might. Mighty Set has force on his side, but young Heru has justice. We shall do justice unto Heru by proclaiming, 'Yes! You shall have the throne of your father!'"

3. Tehuti, Lord of Wisdom, spoke unto the Great Paut Neteru, "This is right a million times!"

4. Auset gave a great cry of joy. She begged the north wind to change direction westward to whisper the news unto Ausar.

5. Lord Shu declared, "Giving the throne unto Heru seems right to the whole of the Paut Neteru!

Tehuti shall give the Royal signet ring to Heru. We shall crown him with the White Crown!"

6. And, to this, Set proclaimed, "It is I who slay the Enemy of Ra daily. It is I who stand in the prow of the Boat of Millions of Years, and no other Neter can do it. It is I who should receive the office of Ausar!"

7. The Neteru knew the terrors of the Serpents of Chaos. They muttered that Set was right. Heru, Lord of Light, spoke and said, "Shall one give office to the uncle when the bodily son is there?"

8. Auset became furious at the Paut Neteru for not speaking in favour of her son. She complained to them until, for the sake of peace, they promised that justice should be given unto Heru.

9. Mighty Set was angered, "How dare you cowards break your oath! I shall fetch my great sceptre and strike one of you down with it each day! I swear that I will not argue my case in any court where Auset is present!"

10. Ra proclaimed, "We shall cross the river to the island in the midst, and try the case thereon. I shall further order the ferryman not to ferry Auset across."

11. Smart and strategic Auset, Nebt Hekau, the Mistress of Magic, changed herself into a bent old woman. She carried a jar of flour and honey cakes. She offered a golden ring to the ferryman to give her passage, and they were soon across. She slipped through the trees, and towards the camp of the Paut Neteru.

12. The Neteru were holding a feast, but Set stood apart from the Paut Neteru. Auset had changed her shape once more. She now appeared as a

beautiful young woman, dressed as a widow. The Great Lady approached the Lord of Storm. "Who are you, my pretty lady?" asked Set, "And why have you come here?"

13. Auset hid her face and wept, "O Great Lord, I am looking for a champion. I was the wife of a herdsman, and I bore for him a son. Then, my dear husband died, and the boy began to tend his father's cattle. But lo, a stranger came and seized our barn, and told my son that he would take our cattle and turn us out. My son wished to protest, but the stranger threatened to beat him. Great Lord, help me! Be my son's champion!"

14. Set heard her words and dried her tears. "Do not cry, my pretty lady. I shall be your champion and destroy this villain! How dare a stranger take the father's property while the son is still alive!"

15. Great Auset shrieked with laughter. She became a kite. She flew into an acacia tree. "Cry yourself, Mighty Set! You have condemned yourself! You have judged your own case!"

16. Set was angered unto tears of rage. The Neteru demanded to know what had happened. He told them of how he had been tricked by the smart Lady Auset.

17. Ra said unto the Dark Neter, "It is true, Set. You have judged yourself."

18. Now the Paut Neteru crossed over the river and camped in the western mountains. Plans were made for the coronation of Heru. Set, still, would not admit his defeat. He exclaimed, "I challenge you, Heru! Let us turn ourselves into hippopotami and fight deep within the river! Whosoever surfaces first shall admit defeat!"

19. Heru accepted gladly, but Auset fell to the ground and wept, afraid that Set would slay her son. The two Neteru plunged into the depths of the river. The battle raged for many days. Victory inclined first to one side, and then to the other, and the heart of Auset suffered bitterly. She took yarn and copper, making them into a magical harpoon. She threw the weapon into the white water. The copper point stabbed Heru in the flank, he surfaced and roared, "Mother! Your spear has pierced me! Let me go!"

20. Auset called to her magic weapon to release Heru. It returned to her hand. She threw it again, and this time it caught hold of Set. With a bellow of pain Set arose. "O my sister, why must you always be my enemy? What have I done to you? I am your brother, Let me go!" Great Auset's heart grew soft, and she released her pleading brother.

21. Heru was furious with his mother for the release of his enemy. He leaped out of the river, his face like a leopard, and cut off the head of Auset with one stroke of his copper knife. He then strode away towards the mountains of the west. Auset, Nebt Hekau, Mistress of Magic, calmly turned her body into a statue, She walked towards the tent of Ra. The Neteru were horrified, even Tehuti Himself. The Great Neter of Wisdom transformed Auset's head and set it again upon her shoulders in the form of a cow. The Paut Neteru went into the mountains of the west in search of Heru.

22. Heru, the young Neter had found an oasis. He was asleep in the shadow of a palm tree. Set found Heru, seized hold of him, threw him down, removed his two eyes from their sockets, and

buried them on the mountain so as to illuminate the earth. The two balls of his eyes became two bulbs which grew into lotuses. When he returned to the encampment, he told the Neteru that he had found no trace of his nephew.

23. Het Heru, Lady of the Southern Sycamore, finally came upon the blinded Neter. She pitied his agony. She caught a gazelle and milked it, and then knelt beside the young Neter, saying gently, "Uncover your face." She dripped the milk onto his wounds. At once the pain vanished. "Open your eyes," commanded Het Heru. He obeyed and found that the healing Magic of the Neter had restored his eyes and he could see again.

24. Het Heru returned to the Paut Neteru and said, "Set has been lying to you. He has torn out the Eyes of Heru. I have healed the young Neter. He approaches now!"

25. Ra called the two contenders before him. He passed judgement upon them for their wrongdoings. He demanded that they cease their quarrelling. Set appeared to agree. He invited Heru to stay with him in his palace.

26. One evening, as the two lay together resting, Set secretly sprayed his semen between the thighs of Heru. He wanted to pretend as if Heru had committed sodomy, because he was trying to emasculate Heru, as this was considered evil and chaos to the people of Kamit and Africa as a whole. It was not the Way of Maat. For Maat was pro-life, and the African people knew that the purpose of life is evolution, and the perpetuation of life itself. Without man and woman coming together as it was designed by Neter, which was

the only true and real sex, there would be no life. Mankind would become extinct. Heru, however, unknown to the Lord of Storm and Chaos, had caught Set's semen in his hand. With the help of his mother, Auset, he placed his own semen upon lettuce growing in Set's garden.

27. Set spoke unto Heru, "Come, let us go, that I may contend with you in the court." Within the court, Set declared, "Let the office of King be given to me, for with regards to Heru who stands here, he has committed sodomy. He is not a real and worthy man. Thus he is not fit to rule Kamit because he is not man enough having done this abominable act, which is against Maat."

28. Heru laughed and said, "What Set has said is false. Let the semen of Set be called, and let us see from where it will answer."

29. And so Tehuti, the Lord of Wisdom, called upon the semen of Set. The answer came from a river, where Auset had long since deposited it.

30. Heru said, "Let mine be called, and let us see from where it will answer."

31. Then Tehuti laid his hand on the arm of Set and said, "Come out, semen of Heru!" And it spoke unto him, "Where shall I come out?" Tehuti said to it, "Come out of his ear." It replied to him, "Should I come out of his ear, I who am divine seed?" Then it came out as a golden sun upon the head of Set. Set became very angry, and he stretched forth his hand to seize the golden sun.

32. In desperation, Set demanded one more contest with Heru. Before the whole Paut Neteru he declared, "Let both of us build a ship of stone. We shall race them down the Nile. Whosoever wins

the race shall wear the Crown of Ausar." Heru agreed to the contest at once.

33.   Mighty Set took up his club. He struck the top of a mountain. Then he built a huge ship of solid stone and dragged it to the river. Heru's ship was already afloat, for the young Neter had secretly made a boat of pine and plastered it so as to appear as stone. Set tried to launch his boat, it sank to the bottom of the Nile and the Paut Neteru laughed. Set leaped into the water. He turned himself into a hippopotamus once more. He attacked the boat of Heru. The wooden boat splintered and sank. Heru grabbed his spear and thrust at Set, but the Paut Neteru shouted at him to stop, he had to obey the command of the Great Neteru of Annu.

34.   Heru made his complaint against Set, "It is now eighty years and we are in the court, but they do not know how to judge among us. I have contended with him in the Hall of Maati. I was found right against him. I have contended with him in the Hall of the Horned Heru. I was found right against him. I have contended with him in the Hall of the Field of Rushes. I was found right against him. I have contended with him in the Hall of the Field Pool. I was found right against him."

35.   In the trial, Ra-Atum asked this important question, "What shall we do about these two Neteru, who for eighty years now, have been before the tribunal?"

36.   Geb, Lord of the Neteru, commanded the Nine Neteru gather to Him. He judged between Heru and Set, he ended their great quarrel. He made Set as King of Southern Kamit, up to the place in

which he was born, which is Su. And Geb made Heru King of Kamit in the land of Northern Kamit, up to the place in which his father was drowned, which is the Division of the Two Lands.

37. Thus Heru stood over one region, and Set stood over one region. They made peace over the Two lands. That was the division of the Two Lands.

38. Geb's words to Set, "Go to the place in which you were born." Set said, "Southern Kamit." Geb's words to Heru, "Go to the place where your father was drowned." Heru said, "Northern Kamit." Geb's words to Heru and Set, "I have separated you. Lower and Upper Kamit."

39. Then Heru spoke and said, "It is not good to defraud me before the Paut Neteru and to take the office of my father Ausar from me!"

40. Shu and Tehuti persuaded the court to send a letter to Ausar. After a time, the messenger returned. He bore an angry letter from the King of the Duat. Ausar demanded to know why his son had been robbed of the throne. He demanded to know if the Neteru had forgotten that it was he, Ausar, who had given the world the precious gifts of barley and wheat.

41. Ra was offended at Ausar's words. He returned a letter of arrogance. After many days, another weary messenger returned. He bore a second letter from the King of the Duat. Tehuti read it aloud, "How good are the deeds of the Paut Neteru? Justice has sunk into the Duat. Now, listen to me, the Duat is full of demons who fear no Neter or Netert. If I send them out into the world of the living they will bring back the hearts of evil-doers to the Duat. Who among you is more powerful

than I? Even the Neteru must come, at last, to the Duat, the Beautiful West." At these words even Ra, the creator, was afraid.

42. Then it seemed wrong to Geb that the portion of Heru was like the portion of Set. So Geb gave to Heru his inheritance, for he is the son of his firstborn son, Ausar.

43. Geb's words to the Nine Neteru, "I have appointed Heru, the firstborn, him alone, Heru, the inheritance. To the son of my son, Heru, goes both Southern Kamit and Northern Kamit."

44. Then Heru stood over the land. He is the uniter of this land, Neb Taui, proclaimed in the great name Ta-tenen, and Lord of Eternity.

45. Then sprouted the two Great Magicians upon his head. He is Heru who arose as King of Upper and Lower Kamit, who united the two lands in the nome of the wall, the place in which the two lands were united.

46. Thus ended the Great Quarrel between the two contenders. Heru came out victorious and avenged his father's death by overthrowing Set and reclaiming the throne. He wore majestically the Unified Crown of both Upper and Lower Kamit.

Chapter 3

TEHUTI'S CHALLENGE

1. A young Heru kneels before Tehuti in a ceremony to receive the go-ahead to fight Set. After years of deliberate preparation, the young Heru has finally reached the top of the mountain in his training.

2. "Before getting my permission, you must pass one more test," says Tehuti. "I am ready," responds Heru, expecting perhaps another round of hard training. "You must answer an important question: What is the true meaning of being Heru Neb Taui?" "The end of my training and defeating Set" says Heru. "A well-deserved victory after defeating Set." Tehuti waits for more. Clearly, he is not happy with Heru's answer. Finally, he responds. "You are not yet ready to fight Set. Come back again in three months."

3. After three months, Heru returns and approaches Tehuti Neb Hu Sia. "What is the true meaning of being Heru Neb Taui?" asks Tehuti. "A just reward for killing Set and avenging the death of my father Ausar" says Heru.

4. Again Tehuti says nothing for a long time, waiting. Surely, it is clear that he is not pleased with Heru's answer. Finally, he responds. "You are still not

ready to fight the Lord of the Fiends, Set. Come back again in three months."

5. Three months come to pass, and Heru approaches Tehuti Up Rehui, once again. Tehuti asks once more: "What is the true meaning of being Heru Neb Taui?"

6. Heru responded, "The title of Neb Taui represents the mastery and control of one's emotions. It means the person is now in control of the animal principle within. The individual can now base all their decisions on Truth, and not on what they like or do not like. All choices are now made based on Maat. The individual lives, thinks, speaks and walks by Maat."

7. Then Tehuti smiled and said, "Finally, the time has come for you to face Set. However, I am now convinced that you will attain victory in this battle, even though it will not be easy."

Chapter 4

STATUE OF HOR–EM–AKHET

1. There was once a prince in Kamit named Thutmose. He was the son of the great Amenhotep and had been named for his grandfather, the Nesu Thutmose III who had succeeded the great queen, Hatshepsut.

2. Because he was the eldest son of Amenhotep, many of his brothers and half-brothers would plot against him, for they desired to be Nesu.

3. They would plot to make Amenhotep think that Thutmose was unworthy to succeed him. They would plot to make him look a fool in front of the people so that they would not want him as Nesu. As he got older they would even plot against his life.

4. But all these plots would fail, for Thutmose honoured the Neteru and the African Ancestors, and so they smiled upon him.

5. Yet Thutmose was troubled in his heart, and these things made him unhappy. He would frequently leave Memphis to go hunt in the desert, or to seek solitude in the mountains.

6. Even when his father wished his presence for a festival or simply to speak to him, Thutmose would stay as short a time as he could and then leave with his trusted servants once more.

7. Amenhotep grieved that his son was unhappy, and prayed to the Neteru that his heart might be lifted.

8. One day, during the great Festival of Ra at Heliopolis, when all of the Nesu's court was present, Thutmose escaped once more, for he wished to see the pyramids of Saqqara, the oldest of them all. He and two servants rode out into the desert where they found the great Step Pyramid of Zoser, the Ancestor of Amenhotep.

9. The next day, they went hunting for gazelle all morning, and when the sun had reached the height of the sky, and the day grew hot, Thutmose and his servants found themselves near the Great Pyramids of Giza, which the Nesu Khufu, Khafre, and Menkaure had built over twelve hundred years before Thutmose was born.

10. Thutmose told his servants to rest at a pool nearby, for he wished to go off for a time that he might offer prayer to his Ancestors.

11. He rode his chariot out to the pyramids, the sun gleaming off their polished sides. He stopped and marvelled at them, knowing that nowhere else was their like equalled, and that at no time since, could anything like them be built.

12. He gazed upon the pyramids for a time and then noticed a huge stone head that rose out of the sand.

13. Thutmose had heard of this marvel, the Statue of Khafre, though he had never seen it before. It was

modelled Heru of the Rising Sun, and a creature of great wisdom and power.

14. During the many ages since the reign of Khafre, the sands had buried it almost completely. Only its head remained above the sand, defying all attempts to hide it forever.

15. Thutmose sat and contemplated the great face, which was said to be the face of Khafre. It wore the headdress of the Nesu, a great crown and veil, with the uraeus cobra and udjat eye, symbols of power, placed in it. He had never seen such terrifying beauty.

16. He prayed to Hor-em-akhet for deliverance from his troubles.

17. When he was finished, there was a rumbling sound, and the sand trembled beneath his feet.

18. Thutmose looked up at Hor-em-akhet and stared, for the head had moved. The statue moved like a great cat attempting to free itself from bonds, and then turned its head toward Thutmose and spoke in a mighty yet kind voice.

19. "Behold, Thutmose, son of Amenhotep, who is Nesu of men by the power of Heru, know that I am Hor-em-akhet, Heru of the Horizon. I am your father, and the father of all Nesus of Kamit. It is your destiny that the Double Crown of Upper and Lower Kamit shall come to you, to be taken up or cast aside as you will."

20. He continued, "Know that if you become Nesu, my blessings will be upon you, and you shall have long life and health all your days. Under your rule, Kamit will become strong and rich, and its people shall never want, for there shall be days of plenty."

21. "You have shown me devotion this day, when my statue is all but forgotten in the desert, and so I have looked kindly upon you. But I ask of you one thing: see how the sand encloses me and hides me from my people? I ask that if you are a good son, that you will help me and free me from the desert sands. Clear away that which holds me fast so that the people may once again come to me and venerate."

22. Then Thutmose was surrounded by light and he knew no more. When he awoke, the Sun Boat of Ra was sinking in the west.

23. He heard the voices of his servants calling to him and he called out that he was alive and well. He looked up and saw the statue lifeless once more, and he remembered the vision.

24. He stood and shouted aloud, "Hor-em-akhet my father! This day I do swear an oath, and I call upon the Neteru and Ancestors to witness it! If I become Nesu, my first command shall be that your sacred image, this statue, shall be freed from the sand and restored to its glory, that all men may come and give you honour!"

25. Thutmose and his servants rode back to Memphis, and from that day forth, all that Thutmose did was blessed. Soon his father Amenhotep named him as heir to the throne, and years later, Thutmose became Nesu.

26. He was regarded as a great Nesu, and the Neteru blessed him all the days of his long life and he was beloved by his people. Kamit did indeed become strong and rich, and there was abundance in all of Kamit.

27. Many millennia came to pass and the Great Statue was found once more buried in the sands by warmongering foreigners, who had come once again with an invading army. They had come to Kamit to plunder it, but had also brought with them scientists, archaeologists, biologists, and all manner of learned men to study Kamit and steal once again its great secrets and civilisation, and claim it as their own, to the whole world.

28. Some years later, an effort was made to clear away the sand from the statue and the pyramids that some portion of their former glory might be seen by all.

29. When the statue was free of the sands the archaeologists found a red granite tablet, that was clearly younger than the statue itself.

30. It was covered in Metu Neter, which could be deciphered, now that the Rosetta Stone had been found. It told the tale of how Prince Thutmose had spoken with the statue long ago, and also gave the proclamation that in the first year of his reign, in the third month, Nesu Thutmose IV had cleared away the sand and restored to greatness, the Hor-em-akhet statue of Khafre. The Neteru and Ancestors were very pleased with him and blessed him to eternity, for he had fulfilled his role as an African descendant, by taking care of them and their shrines, culture and traditions.

Chapter 5

THE DIVINE CHILD

1. She dreamed a dream of herself. They were speaking to her saying: "Are you Meh-wesekht, the wife of Setme, who lies in vain, seeking to receive healing? When the morning of tomorrow has come, go to the entrance of the rooms of urinating of Setme your husband. Behold! You shall find a vine of melon that grows there. Wound it with its gourds, and you shall put it back and you shall make it into medicine, and you shall cause a child to be born. You will conceive from his semen in the night named."

2. Meh-wesekht awoke from the dream, and these were the things that she had seen. She acted according to everything that she had been told in her dream: she lay down by the side of Setme, her husband, and she conceived from his semen. There came her time. Behold! She showed the signs of women who are pregnant. Setme made the announcement of it before the Nesu. His heart was exceedingly glad because of it. He bound on her an amulet, he read to her writing. Setme laid himself down one night and dreamed a dream, in which they spoke to him, saying: "Me-wesekht,

your wife, has conceived in the night. The child that will be born shall be named Sa-Ausar. Numerous are the marvels that he shall do in this beautiful land of Kamit."

3.   Setme awoke from the dream, and these were the things that he had seen. His heart was exceedingly glad. She lived patiently through her months of pregnancy, and she did it whilst exceedingly glad. Then came her time of giving birth, she bore a male child. They let Setme know about it. He named him Sa-Ausar, according with what had been said in the dream that he kept in his heart.

4.   After the pregnancy and after he was born, they nurtured him. It happened that when the child Sa-Ausar was one year old, people might have said that he was two years old. When he was two years old, they might have said that he was three years of age. Setme never passed an hour without looking at the child Sa-Ausar. The love that he had for him was very great. He grew big and strong, and was sent to school.

5.   At school, he rivalled the scribe who had been appointed to give him instruction. The child Sa-Ausar grew and he began to learn magic with the scribes of the House of Life in the temple of Ptah. He made wonder of the world at him, and Setme loved the fact that the Nesu should order him to be taken before him, and that he should be presented to them, all. And on a certain day it happened that Setme was purified for meeting with the Nesu according to tradition. The child Sa-Ausar was going to meet the Nesu as well.

6.   On their way to meet with the Nesu, Setme heard the voice of a wailing and he looked beside him

and witnessed a rich man's funeral, as they were carrying him out to the desert. The wailing was verily loud. Much being the glory in which he was compared to that in which he himself was. He gazed again, and he looked at his feet. Behold! He saw a poor man being carried out from Memphis to the cemetery. He was wrapped in a mat, there was no man on earth who was walking after him. Said Setme: "By Ptah, the great Neter, how much better it shall be in Amenti for the great men who they glorify with loud wailing compared to poor men whom they take to the desert without the glory of a funeral."

7. But Sa-Ausar said: "You shall be treated in Amenti like this poor man will be treated in Amenti. That which shall be done to this rich man in Amenti shall not be done to you. You shall go into Amenti to witness what happens there."

8. Sa-Ausar took him directly to the fourth hall in Amenti, he explained to him that the first three halls were better seen when it was time for one to see them, not before or after that allocated time. His father reluctantly agreed and understood what his son admonished him about.

9. So they entered the fourth hall of Amenti. Setme saw some men that were scattered and separated, and great at eating besides. There were some others as well, their provision, water and bread, was hung over them. They were running to take it down, but some others were digging pits at their feet to prevent them from reaching it.

10. They entered the fifth hall and behold! Setme saw the noble spirits, standing in their positions, and those who were accused of violence, were

standing at the entrance praying. The bolt of the door of the fifth hall was being fixed in the right eye of a man, who was praying and uttering loud lamentation.

11. They went into the sixth hall, and Setme saw the Neteru of the council of the inhabitants of Amenti standing in their order of standing. The attendants of Amenti were standing, making a proclamation.

12. They went into the seventh hall, and Setme saw the figure of the great Neter Ausar. He was seated upon his throne of good gold, crowned with the Atef, the great Neter Anpu was on his left, the great Neter Tehuti on his right. The Neteru of the council of the inhabitants of Amenti were standing to the left and right of him. The balance was set in the middle before them. They were weighing the evil deeds against the good deeds. The great Neter Tehuti was writing, Anpu was giving the word to his colleague.

13. The law was that he who was found to have done more evil deeds than good ones was thrown to Ammit of the Lord of Amenti, who destroyed his soul and his body and did not allow him to breathe ever again. The law was that, he who was found to have committed more numerous good deeds than evil deeds was taken to the Neteru of the council of the Lord of Amenti, and his soul went with the noble spirits. The law was that he who was found to have committed as many good deeds as evil deeds, was taken amongst the excellent spirits that serve Seker-Ausar.

14. And Setme saw a great man clothed in raiment of byssus who was near the place where Ausar

was. His position was elevated. Setme marvelled at the things that he saw in Amenti. Sa-Ausar walked out in front of him and said to him: "My father Setme, don't you see this great man, who is clothed in garment of byssus and is near the place where Ausar is? That poor man whom you saw, being carried out from Memphis, and not a man walking after him. That is the same man that was wrapped in a mat. They brought him to the Duat, and they weighed his good deeds that he had done upon earth. They found that his good deeds had been more numerous than his evil deeds, according to the measure of his term of life that Tehuti determined should be allotted to him, according to the measure of his greatness of eye upon earth. It was commanded before Ausar that the burial outfit of that rich man whom you saw being carried out from Memphis, the praise that was made of him being great, be given to this poor man named, and that they should take him amongst the noble spirits as a man of Neter who follows Seker-Ausar, he being near to the place in which is Ausar.

15. That great man whom you saw, they took him to Amenti, they weighed his evil deeds against his good deeds. They found that his evil deeds were more numerous than the good deeds that he did upon earth. It was commanded to imprison him in Amenti. He is that man that you saw with the bolt of the gate of Amenti being fixed on his right eye. They were shutting and opening out on his eye, his mouth was open in loud lamentation. By the great Neter Ausar, Lord of Amenti, behold! I say to you upon earth: "There shall be done to

you just as is being done to this poor man, there shall not be done to you according to which is being done to that great man, and I know what will become of him."

16. Setme said: "My son Sa-Ausar, many are the marvels that I have seen in Amenti. In the course of time, tell me what has happened to these men who are scattered apart, who are great at eating? In addition, some men whose provision, water, and bread, was hung above them, were running to bring it down, while some other men were digging pits at their feet to prevent them reaching it. What of them?"

17. Sa-Ausar said: "It is a just word, my father Setme, these men whom you saw who were scattered and apart, who were great at eating in addition. They are like the men who are on earth, who are under the curse of the Neter. They work night and day for their livelihood, their women rob them. In addition, they find no bread to eat. They came to Amenti again. They found their evil deeds to be more numerous than their good deeds. They found that what had become of them on earth, they became in Amenti."

18. "Concerning those other men whom you saw, whose food, water and bread is hung over them, and who are running to bring it down, while some men are digging a pit at their feet to prevent them from reaching it. The kind of men that are on earth, whose life is before them, the Neter is digging a pit at their feet to prevent their finding it. They came to Amenti. They allowed that which had become of them on the earth to become of them again in Amenti. Behold! They received

their soul in the Duat. Find it in your heart, my father Setme, namely, that he who is good upon the earth, they are good to him in Amenti, while he who is evil, they are evil to him."

19. "These matters are established, they shall not be changed ever. The things that you see in the Duat in Memphis happen in those 42 nomes in which are the assessors of the great Neter Ausar. They happen in Abydos, the place of the oracle, the dwelling of princes, and in Philae."

20. Sa-Ausar ended these words spoken before his father. He went upon the desert of Memphis, his father Setme embracing him, his hand was in his hand. Setme asked saying: "My son Sa-Ausar, separate is the place down there where we are going, separate is the place from which we have come up."

21. Sa-Ausar did not answer Setme even with one word. Setme marvelled at the words that he had heard, saying: "He will be able to become like the noble spirits as a man of Neter." I was walking with him, saying: "This is my son." Setme marvelled at the things he had seen in Amenti which weighed upon him heavily since he was not able to reveal them to any man on earth.

22. Behold! The boy Sa-Ausar passed twelve years and there was no good scribe or learned man who rivalled him in Memphis in reading or registering pledges.

Chapter 6

REINCARNATION

1. One day, the Nesu Osirmare went to the court of his house in Memphis. The council, the princes, the generals, the great men of Kamit were standing according to their rank at court. They came saying: "This is a communication that Anate of Ethiopia made about a sealed letter carried on his body."

2. The announcement of it was made before the Nesu. He was brought to the court and prayed: "Is there someone who reads this letter which I have brought to Kamit before the Nesu without spoiling its seal, who will read the writing in it without opening it. Should there be no good scribe and learned man in Kamit who is able to read it without opening it, I will take the humiliation of Kamit to the land of Nehes, my country."

3. When the Nesu heard these words with his princes they said: "By the great Neter Ptah, is there the strength in the hand of a good scribe and learned man to read the writings of a letter without opening it?"

4. Said the Nesu: "Let there be summoned Setme Khamwesy my son." They ran and brought him at that instant. He bowed to the ground. He saluted

the Nesu. He raised himself, stood on his feet, making the blessings of the salutation of the Nesu.

5. The Nesu said to him: "My son Setme, have you heard the words that Anate of Ethiopia has said before me, 'Is there a good scribe or learned man in Kamit who shall be able to read this letter that is in my hand without breaking its seal, and shall know what is written in it without opening it?'"

6. When Setme heard these words, he did not know the place on earth where he was, and he said: "My great lord, who is he that shall be able to read writing without opening it? Give me ten days of delay that I may see what I shall be able to do, to prevent the humiliation of Kamit being reported in the land of Nehes, the country of eaters of gum."

7. The Nesu rose from court, his heart was heavy with grief. He lay down without drinking and eating. Setme went to his apartments without knowing the place in the world he was going to. He covered himself with his clothes from head to foot, not knowing the place on earth in which he was.

8. His wife Meh-wesekht was informed of it. She came to the place where Setme was. She reached inside his clothes and did not find any warmth. He lay quiet in his clothes.

9. She said to him: "My brother Setme, there is no warmth in your lap, but sadness of heart." He said to her: "Do not bother me, my sister Mewesekht, the matter on account of which my heart is grieved is not a thing that it is right to reveal to a woman." The child Sa-Ausar came in. He stood over Setme his father and said to him: "My father Setme,

what are you lying here for with a sad heart? Tell me the things that are enclosed in your heart that I may make them cease."

10. He said: "Don't bother me my son Sa-Ausar, about the things in my heart. You are young of age, you are not grown yet, look after yourself." Sa-Ausar said: "Tell me so I may lighten your heart." Setme said: "My son Sa-Ausar, Anate of Ethiopia has come to Kamit, carrying a sealed letter on his body and he says, 'Is there somebody who will read it without opening it? And if there is no good scribe and learned man in Kamit who is able to read it, I will carry the news of the humiliation of Kamit to the land of Nehes, my country.' Behold! I lay down with my heart saddened because of this, my son Sa-Ausar."

11. When Sa-Ausar heard these words he laughed for a long time. Setme said to him: "Why are you laughing?" He answered: "I am laughing because you are lying, telling me that your heart is sad because of a small matter like this one. Get up, my father Setme, I shall be able to read the letter that was brought to Kamit without opening it and to know what is written in it without breaking its seal." When Setme heard these words he got up at once and said: "What is your pledge that you are speaking the truth, my son Sa-Ausar?" He said to him: "My father Setme, go to the apartments on the ground floor. With every book you take out of the case, I will tell you what book it is, and I will read it, without seeing it, standing above you in your apartments on the ground floor."

12. Setme got up and stood on his feet. He did everything that Sa-Ausar had said to him.

Sa-Ausar read every book that Setme his father lifted up, without opening them. Setme came up from the apartments on the ground floor and his joy was boundless.

13. He hurried to the place where the Nesu was. He related before him everything that the child Sa-Ausar had said to him. His heart was very glad because of it. The Nesu washed himself for feasting with Setme. He ordered Sa-Ausar to be brought to the feast before him. They drank and made merry.

14. The morning of the next day came. The Nesu came forth to the court between his great men. The Nesu ordered Anate of Ethiopia to be fetched. He was brought to the court. The sealed letter was still on his body. He stood in the middle of the court.

15. The child Sa-Ausar advanced to the centre and stood near Anate of Ethiopia. He spoke against him: "Woe! Wicked one of Ethiopia, may Amen his Neter, smite him! You have come up to Kamit, the beautiful garden of Ausar, the footstool of Ra-Herukhuti, the beautiful horizon of the souls, saying, 'I will report its humiliation to the land of Nehes.' The inspiration of your Neter Amen is cast on thee. The words that I shall narrate are written in this letter. Do not utter falsehoods concerning them before the Nesu, your sovereign!"

16. When Anate of Ethiopia looked at the child Sa-Ausar standing in the court, he put his head to the ground. He said: "I will not speak falsehood concerning any word that you will say."

17. Sa-Ausar began relating before the Nesu and his nobles, and the people of Kamit paid close

attention to what he said: "What is written in the letter of Anate of Ethiopia who is standing in our midst is as follows: Once upon a time in the days of the Nesu Menkh-pa-Ra Si-Amen who ruled as the beneficent king of the whole land. Kamit was overflowing with everything in his time. He was abundant in giving expenditure, and work in the great temples of Kamit.

18. There happened a day, that the King of the land of Nehes making leisure in the fields of the land of Amen. Behold! He heard the voice of three men of Ethiopia. One of them said in a loud voice: 'That Amen may not find for me evil nor the King of Kamit cause abomination to be done to me. I would cast my magic up to Kamit that I might cause the people of Kamit to pass three days and three nights without seeing light.'

19. Said the other of them after saying: 'Let Amen not find for me misfortune nor the King of Kamit cause abomination to be done to me. I would cast my magic up to Kamit that I might cause the Nesu of Kamit to be brought to the land of Nehes, and cause him to be beaten with a scourging, 500 blows of the stick in the midst, before the Viceroy, and cause him to be brought back up to Kamit in six hours precisely.'

20. When the viceroy heard what the three men of Ethiopia had said, he ordered them to be brought before him. He said to them: 'Who of you is he that said, "I will cast my magic up to Kamit, I will not allow them to see light in three days and three nights?"' They said: 'It is Hor, the son of the Sow.'

21. Said he: 'Who is he that said, "I will cast my magic up to Kamit, I will bring Nesu to the land

of Nehes, I will cause him to be beaten with a scourging, 500 blows of the stick in the midst of the Viceroy, I will cause him to be taken back to Kamit in six hours precisely?'" They said: 'It is Hor, the son of the Nubian.'

22. He said: 'Who is he that said, "I will cast my magic up in Kamit. I will not allow the land to be fertile until three years?"' They said: 'It is Hor, the son of the Princess.'

23. The Viceroy said to Hor, the son of the Nubian: 'Do your feat of magic in writing. By the life of Amen, the bull of Meroe my Neter, if your hand will satisfy me, I will shower you with an abundance of good things.'

24. Hor, the son of the Nubian, made of wax a group of four runners, he read some Hekau to them, he gave them the Breath of Life, he made them come alive.

25. He commanded them: 'Go up to Kamit and bring the Nesu of Kamit to the place where the Viceroy is. He shall be beaten with a scourging, 500 blows of the stick before the Viceroy, and then you will take him back up to Kamit in six hours.' They said: 'Certainly. We will not let anything go amiss.' The sorceries of the Ethiopian proceeded up to Kamit by night, they overpowered the Nesu Menkh-pa-Ra Si-Amen, they took him to the land of Nehes, to the place where the Viceroy was. He was beaten with scourging, 500 blows of the stick, before the Viceroy, then they returned him up to Kamit in six hours precisely."

26. Sa-Ausar finished narrating the story before the Nesu and his princes, and the people of Kamit heard his voice. He said: "The inspiration of

your Neter Amen is cast on you. Are the words I have recounted those that are written in the letter which is in your hand?"

27. Anate of Ethiopia said: "Continue reading! Every word you have said is true."

28. Sa-Ausar said to Nesu: "After these things had happened, they returned the Nesu Si-Amen up to Kamit, his hinder parts beaten with many lashes. He lay down in the shrine of Per-Hor his hinder parts hurting from the cruel beating. The morning of the next day arrived. The Nesu said to his courtiers: 'What has happened in Kamit when I was made to depart from it?'

29. Shame on the words of the courtiers who said: 'Probably the Nesu has lost his mind.' They said: 'You are well, you are well, O Nesu, our great lord. The great Neter Auset will stop your troubles. What is the meaning of the words that you have said before us, O Nesu, our great lord? You were lying down in the shrine of Per-Hor, the Neteru protect you.' The Nesu got up, showed his courtiers his back which had been beaten exceedingly and he said: 'By the life of the great Neter Ptah, someone took me to the land of Nehes in the night, someone beat me with 500 blows of the stick before the Viceroy, and they returned me up to Kamit in six hours.'

30. When they saw the hinder parts of the Nesu which had been beaten cruelly, they made a great noise. Menkh-pa-Ra Si-Amen had a librarian who was called Hor, son of Pa-neshe, who was a highly learned man. He came to the palace where the Nesu was and he exclaimed: 'My great lord, these were the sorceries of the Ethiopians. By the life of

your servant, I will order them to be thrown into your house of torment and execution.'

31. The Nesu said to him: 'Come quickly to me! Don't let me be taken to the land of Nehes another night.' The librarian Hor, son of Pa-neshe, came at once. He took his books and amulets to the place where the Nesu was. He read Hekau to him and fastened an amulet on him to prevent the sorceries of the Ethiopians from getting power over him. He left the Nesu, taking his offerings and libations, and went on board a boat and sailed to Khmun without delay. He went into the temple of Khmun, he made his offerings and libations before Tehuti the great, the great lord of Khmun, the great Neter.

32. He said a prayer before him: 'Look upon me favourably, my lord Tehuti. Let not the Ethiopians report the humiliation of Kamit to the land of Nehes. It is you who created magic in writing. You suspended the heaven, established the earth, the Duat, and placed the Neteru among the stars. Let me know how to save the Nesu from the sorceries of the Ethiopians.'

33. Hor, son of Pa-neshe, lay down in the temple. He dreamed a dream that night in which the great Neter Tehuti spoke to him: 'Are you Hor, son of Pa-neshe, the librarian of Nesu Menkh-pa-Ra Si-Amen? When the morning of tomorrow comes, go to the library of the temple of Khmun. You shall find a shrine which is closed and sealed. Open it. You shall find a box in that shrine. There is a roll of papyrus in it, which I wrote with my own hand. Bring it up, make a copy of it, and return it to its place. Its name is 'The Magic Book

of Tehuti'. It protected me from the impious. It shall protect the Nesu that he may be saved from the sorceries of the Ethiopians.'

34. Hor, son of Pa-neshe, awoke from the dream. He remembered what he had seen. It was in the hand of the Neter. He did everything according to what he had been told in his dream. He hurried to the place where the Nesu was. He made for him an amulet against sorceries in writing. The next day arrived.

35. The sorceries of Hor, the son of the Nubian, returned to Kamit by night, to the place where the Nesu was. They returned to the place where the Viceroy was at that time. They could not get power over the Nesu because of the amulets with the Hekau that the librarian Hor, son of Pa-neshe, had bound upon him. The morning of the next day arrived.

36. The Nesu told the librarian Hor, son of Pa-neshe, about everything that he had seen by night, and how the sorceries of the Ethiopians had turned away, unable to get power over him. Hor, son of Pa-neshe, ordered pure and abundant wax brought to him. He made a group of four bearers. He pronounced Hekau over them. He gave them the Breath of Life. He made them come alive. He commanded them: 'Go to the land of Nehes tonight. Bring the Viceroy up to Kamit, to the place where the Nesu is. After he has been beaten with 500 blows of the stick before the Nesu, you shall return him to the land of Nehes in six hours.'

37. They said: 'Certainly, we will not let anything go amiss.' The sorceries of Hor, son of Pa-neshe, travelled under the clouds of heaven, they hurried

to the land of Nehes by night. They overpowered the Viceroy. They brought him up to Kamit. He was beaten with 500 blows of the stick before the Nesu. They returned him to the land of Nehes in six hours, all the way."

38. Sa-Ausar narrated this story before Nesu and his nobles, the people of Kamit heard his voice, saying: "The power of your Neter Amen is cast upon you, O wicked one from Ethiopia. The words I have spoken, are they written in this letter?" The Ethiopian, his head turned to the ground, said: "Continue reading! Every word you have spoken is written in this letter."

39. Sa-Ausar said: "After all these events had happened, after they had brought back the Viceroy to the land of Nehes in six hours, they put him in his place, he lay down. He rose in the morning, badly beaten by the blows that had been given him above in Kamit. 'They beat me with 500 blows of the stick before the Nesu of Kamit. They returned me to the land of Nehes.'

40. He turned his back towards the princes, they uttered loud lamentations. The Viceroy ordered them to go after Hor, son of the Nubian. He said: 'May Amen curse you, the bull of Meroe, my Neter! You went to the men of Kamit, consider and let me see the method with which you will save me from the hand of Hor, son of Pa-neshe.'

41. He made his sorceries and bound them on the Viceroy to save him from the sorceries of Hor, son of Pa-neshe. The night of the next day came.

42. The sorceries of Hor, son of Pa-neshe, travelled to the land of Nehes. They carried the Viceroy up to Kamit. He was beaten with 500 blows of

the stick before Nesu. He was taken back to the land of Nehes in six hours all told. This happened to the Viceroy for three days, the sorceries of the Ethiopians were not able to save the Viceroy from the hand of Hor, son of Pa-neshe. The Viceroy was in deepest anguish. He ordered Hor, the son of the Nubian, to be brought to him.

43. He said to him: 'Woe, you enemy from Ethiopia, you have caused me to be humiliated by hand of the men of Kamit. You could not save me from their hands. By the life of Amen, the bull of Meroe my Neter, should it be that you should not be able to save me from the men of Kamit, I will order them to put you to an evil death.' He said: 'My master, the Viceroy, send me up to Kamit that I may meet him who does magic among them, that I may strive against him, that I may let him see the scorn that is in my heart for his skill.'

44. Hor, the son of the Nubian, was sent away from before the Viceroy. He came to the place where his mother the Nubian was. She said: 'You are going up to Kamit to do sorcery there, beware of the men of Kamit. You will not be able to contend with them. Don't let yourself be caught by their hands, so that you will not return to the land of Nehes forever.' He said: 'There is nothing to what you are saying. I shall not be able to avoid going up to Kamit in order to cast my magic on it.'

45. The Nubian, his mother said to him: 'Should it happen that you do go to Kamit, let us agree on some signs between me and you. Should you fail I will come to you in order to see whether I'll be able to save you.' He said to her: 'Should I be overcome, then when you drink or eat flesh, the

water before you will turn the colour of blood, the food that is before you will turn the colour of flesh, the sky shall turn the colour of blood before your eyes.'

46. Hor, the son of the Nubian, having set the signs between himself and his mother, went up to Kamit, crammed with magic. He traversed from that which Amen made as far as Memphis, to the place where the Nesu was, hunting after him who was doing magic in Kamit. He came to the court, stood before the Nesu and spoke in a loud voice: 'Behold! You who do magic against me in the court of the Nesu, while the people of Kamit look at me. You devious scribe from the House of Life, you haughty scribe from the House of Life, who cast magic spells on the Viceroy, who bring him up to Kamit, in spite of me.'

47. As he was speaking these words, Hor, son of Pa-neshe was standing in the court before the Nesu. He said: 'Behold! Enemy from Ethiopia, are you not Hor, son of the Nubian, whom I saved in the reeds of Ra, with your companion from Ethiopia who accompanied you, you were drowning in the water, you were cast down from the hill on the east of On? Did you not repent the freeing of the Nesu, your sovereign, after you had caused his hinder parts to be beaten in the place where the Viceroy was? You have come up to Kamit, asking: "Is he who does magic against me, here?" By the life of Atum, lord of On, the Neteru of Kamit have brought you to requite you in their country.'

48. When Hor, son of the Nubian, heard the words spoken by Hor, son of Pa-neshe, he answered him:

'Is it he to whom I taught jackal-language who does sorcery against me?' The man of Ethiopia made an effort to cast a written spell: he caused fire to come out in the court. The Nesu with the princes of Kamit uttered a loud cry: 'Hasten to our side, librarian Hor, son of Pa-neshe!' Hor, son of Pa-neshe, cast a written spell. He caused the sky to open up with southern rain over the flame. It was extinguished in an instant.

49. The Ethiopian made another effort of magic in writing. He created a great covering over the court. No one could see his brother or his companion. Hor, son of Pa-neshe, read a spell to the sky. He caused it to cease. It cleared from the evil wind. Hor, the son of the Nubian, made another effort of written magic.

50. He caused a great vault of stone, 200 cubits in length by 50 cubits of width, to appear above the Nesu and his princes, with the intention to leave Kamit without a king, the world deficient of a sovereign. The Nesu looked at the sky, he saw the vault of stone above him. He opened his mouth and uttered a loud cry, together with the people that were in court.

51. Hor, son of Pa-neshe, said a Heka which caused an air-boat of papyrus to appear, and it proceeded with the vault of stone. Behold! It flew with it forward to the Mighty Pool, the great water of Kamit.

52. The man of Ethiopia knew that he was not able to contend with the Kamitian. He made an effort to cast a written spell to prevent people seeing him in court, with the intent of translating himself to the land of Nehes, his city. Hor, son of Pa-neshe,

pronounced a spell causing the sorceries of the Ethiopian to be revealed, causing the Nesu to see him, with the people of Kamit that were standing in the court. He was in the form of a fox-gander and was about to depart.

53. Hor, son of Pa-neshe, pronounced a spell causing him to turn back, and there was a fowler standing over him, his piercing knife in his hand. He was going to do to it an abomination. After all these things had happened, the signs which Hor, son of the Nubian, had set between himself and his mother, they all happened in front of her eyes. She immediately went up to Kamit, taking on the form of a fox-goose. She stood over the palace of the Nesu bewailing her son with her voice, while he was in the form of a fox-gander and the fowler was standing over him.

54. Hor, son of Pa-neshe, looked at the sky, He saw the Nubian in the guise in which she was. He knew that it was the Nubian. He pronounced a spell causing her to be turned on her back with a fowler standing over her about to kill her with his knife. She changed from the form in which she was. She took on the guise of a Nubian woman, praying: 'Do not make an end to us, Hor, son of Pa-neshe, let go of us from this occasion of failure. Should you give us an aerial boat, we will not return to Kamit ever.'

55. Hor, son of Pa-neshe, swore an oath by the Nesu and the Neteru of Kamit, saying: 'I will not remove my spell, until you have sworn an oath to me not to return up to Kamit for any kind of purpose.' The Nubian raised her hand and swore not to come up to Kamit for all eternity. Hor, the

son of the Nubian, swore an oath, saying: 'I will not come up to Kamit for 1500 years.' Hor, son of Pa-neshe withdrew his hand from his written spell. He gave an aerial boat to Hor, the son of the Nubian, and the Nubian, his mother. They proceeded to the land of Nehes, their city."

56. Sa-Ausar made this narration before the Nesu, the people of Kamit heard his voice. Setme, his father, saw everything. The head of the man from Ethiopia was facing the ground. Sa-Ausar said: "By the life of your face, my great lord, this man who is standing before you, is Hor, the son of the Nubian. This man, whose words I am relating, who has not repented of those things that he did long ago, has come up to Kamit at the end of 1500 years to cast the sorceries here. By the life of Ausar, great good lord of Amenti, before whom I rest, I am Hor, son of Pa-neshe, this man who stands before Nesu, found this out, that the wicked one of Ethiopia would cast his sorceries up into it and there would be no good scribe and learned man in Kamit at the time able to contend with him."

57. "I prayed before Ausar in Amenti to let me come forth to the world again, to prevent reporting the humiliation of Kamit to the land of Nehes. Ausar commanded to bring me out into the world. I awoke. I flew to the crown of the head to find Setme, the son of Nesu, upon the hill of Memphis. I grew as this vine with the intent of returning to the body again, that I might be born to the world to do magic against this enemy from Ethiopia who stands in court."

58. Hor, son of Pa-neshe, in the shape of Sa-Ausar, cast a written spell on the man of Ethiopia. He caused the fire to surround him. It consumed him in the middle of the court. The Nesu saw him together with the nobles and the people of Kamit. Sa-Ausar passed away as a shadow from the company of the Nesu and Setme, his father. They did not see him. The Nesu marvelled with his great men at the things they had seen in the court and they said: "There is no good scribe and learned man like Hor, son of Pa-neshe. There will not be like this ever."

59. Setme opened his mouth and shouted loudly when Sa-Ausar had passed away as a shadow, and he had not seen him. The Nesu rose from court, anger in his heart at the things that he had seen. He started preparations to be made before Setme to lodge him because of Sa-Ausar, his son, to refresh his heart. When evening fell Setme went to his apartments, his heart exceedingly sad. Meh-wesekht lay at his side. She conceived from him that night. She did not delay and gave birth to a male child, who was given the name of Wesy-Ment-Hor. Setme did not cease to make offerings and libations before the genius of Hor, son of Pa-neshe, at every occasion.

60. And so the time of troubles came to pass, as do all times pass, only to come back again.

Chapter 7

SONS OF HERU

1. The village of Shekhem, in the south of Kamit, known for its powerful and well trained warriors, was facing several deadly problems, as the villagers had become gravely ill. To add salt to injury, the local medicine and herbs were rendered useless, and failed to heal any of the deeply afflicted people. This had been going on for the past three months.

2. The village had failed time and time again to resolve this difficult problem. The village elders decided to consult the village of Khukhem, in the north of Kamit, which was well known worldwide for its wisdom and intelligence. They sent a special envoy with gifts to go and consult Ti-Maa, the famous and Wise Priestess of Khukhem.

3. After three days and three nights of travelling, the special envoy arrived at Khukhem. They went straight to the Chief of Khukhem and gave him the message from the elders and Chief of Shekhem. The message was very simple and called for help and described the dire situation that the village of Shekhem found itself in.

4.   The chief gave them permission to go and see Ti-Maa, the Wise Priestess of Khukhem. In return, the envoy presented some of the gifts to the Chief and his Council. The Chief commanded a little boy and girl to show the visitors where Ti-Maa, the Wise Priestess lived.

5.   When they got to the Temple, they were instructed to wash and bathe with frankincense and myrrh before they approached Ti-Maa, the Wise Priestess. The visitors gladly obliged and adhered to the protocol as they were used to such procedures for approaching sacred spaces and places. The ancient understanding was that, "none but the pure must approach the pure."

6.   After they finished washing they were ushered into the Outer Temple where Ti-Maa, the Wise Priestess, was seated waiting for them. This is where Ti-Maa, the Wise Priestess, would see the general public, who were restricted to the Outer Temple. Only Initiates were allowed to go into the Inner Temple.

7.   As soon as they were seated, she asked them, "Do you know what I am going to tell you?" They responded, "No." And immediately, they interjected, "But you don't even know why we are here." She smiled and said, "My good friends it is my sacred duty to know all matters that need to be known. For it was already written before it even happened." They started fidgeting and looked puzzled by what she was saying. Then one of them asked, "Well, in that case, what is your advice, what should we do about what made us cross so many rivers and so many mountains? Please help our village which has been stricken

with this sad state of affairs. I'm afraid that if we continue like this, there will be nothing left of our village."

8. Ti-Maa, the Wise Priestess, responded and said, "Well there is no need to panic. Every now and then, there is an imbalance caused by bad Hekau in the world, and dark spirits wreak havoc on innocent people." She continued, "Take these four canopic jars. They contain the power of each of the children of Heru who sprung from the lotus flower in primordial waters. It was Sebek who pulled each one out and safely positioned them on the river banks. They will protect thee from the legions of Apep and Set. Listen to my instructions very carefully and your village will be set free from strife."

9. She took out the first jar, with a head shaped like a human, from her Bag of Hekau, and said, "Take this jar of Imset, it will protect the livers of the people and place it on the southernmost part of the village. Make sure that you bury it deep underground where no one will find it. Chant four times, 'Tua Imset Sa Heru.' Do not look back. It will protect thy village."

10. Ti-Maa, the Wise Priestess, took out a second jar, with a head shaped like a baboon, from her Bag of Hekau, and said, "Take this jar of Hapi, it will protect the lungs of the people and place it on the northernmost part of the village. Make sure that you bury it deep underground where no one will find it. Chant four times, 'Tua Hapi Sa Heru.' Do not look back. It will protect thy village."

11. She took out a third jar, with a head shaped like a jackal, from her Bag of Hekau, and said, "Take

this jar of Duamutef, it will protect the stomach of the people and place it on the easternmost part of the village. Make sure that you bury it deep underground where no one will find it. Chant four times, 'Tua Duamutef Sa Heru.' Do not look back. It will protect thy village."

12. Finally, Ti-Maa, the Wise Priestess, took out a fourth and last jar, with a head shaped like a falcon, from her Bag of Hekau, and said, "Take this jar of Khebsenuf, it will protect the intestines of the people and place it on the westernmost part of the village. Make sure that you bury it deep underground where no one will find it. Chant four times, 'Tua Khebsenuf Sa Heru.' Do not look back. It will protect thy village."

13. She then cautioned them and stressed, "If you follow my instructions accurately, this dark cloud that has befallen your village will be lifted, after exactly seven days and nights. No longer will your people be sick inexplicably. From this day forth, the herbs of Shekhem will be able to heal all ailments. But make sure that these jars are never removed, for it will allow the dark spirits to come and attack you again."

14. When Ti-Maa, the Wise Priestess, was finished, the special envoy stood up, opened their gift bag, and presented her with the rest of the gifts. They did not say 'thank you' to her, for it was tradition not to say 'thank you,' when presented with Juju, by Ti-Maa, the Wise Priestess. They immediately left for the village of Shekhem. They travelled by day and night, and were in a hurry to get back to the village before irreparable damage was done.

15. When the envoy got to the village of Shekhem they followed the instructions carefully that they received from the Priestess of Khukhem. Seven days and nights passed, and just as the Priestess had advised, the people of Shekhem were cured of all their ailments, and life became normal again.

16. The people celebrated and thanked the Neteru and the Ancestors for showing them the old African ways of resolving problems. They went as far as building a statue of Ti-Maa, the Wise Priestess of Khukhem, in order to remind them of the wisdom, intelligence and power of the Neteru and Ancestors. They all vowed to never forget the blessings and protection they receive, from those that cannot be seen but are always with us, and guiding us from the Duat.

Chapter 8

HERU NEJ ATEF

1. When Heru grew up, he devoted himself solely to the duty of "avenger of his father." When he became of age, he started to assemble an Army in order to fight Set and dethrone him. But it was inopportune and difficult for him to achieve his mission. Many of his African people simply laughed, ridiculed and taunted him, and were not willing to fight for him, because they feared Set and his technological prowess and might, and thought he would easily annihilate and vanquish Heru, regardless of the fact that he was the son of Ausar, the late King. However, he did not try to debate the naysayers, instead he just focused on executing his Vision. He found comfort in what Tehuti had taught him, "Leave him in error, he who loves his error." It kept him motivated and he never attempted to convince the naysayers otherwise. He paid them no attention, for they were a mere fruitless distraction.

2. However, amidst the ridicule, he was able to convince the relevant and useful Africans that he needed to begin the long journey and fulfil his mission. These people would form part of his

Military Council. They would become his Inner Circle that he would entrust with his plans for the future. The Nine Souls that Heru was able to convince are: Akhu, Shekhem, Ba, Ab, Sahu, Ren, Ka, Khaibit and Khab.

3. Akhu was the source of universal intelligence and wisdom, and had a highly evolved intuition. He could shed light in any situation. He provided the light that showed the way. He injected optimism into the nascent army.

4. Shekhem was the source of universal power. She was very powerful and could manipulate energy when needed, to make things happen. She motivated everyone to push forward and deliver what was required to win this war.

5. Ba was a combination of intelligence and power, an individuation of the two. He embodied both Akhu's and Shekhem's skills. He was proficient in strategy and was going to be useful in crafting military strategy against Set's Army. He would become Heru's second-in-command. In essence, he was just as wise as his father, Ausar, so Heru trusted him very much with everything. He was the active Soul of the Army.

6. Ab was brilliant at crafting choices and scenarios to any given situation, no matter how dire, without being emotional. He was convinced that there was a solution to every problem, one only needed to spend enough time searching for one. To that end, he would work closely with Ba in developing the relevant strategies. Ab was very willing to assist any of the other Army members with their tasks. He was the enlightened Will of

the Army. His motto was, "Where there's a Will, there's a Way." He lived by it.

7. Sahu was the most experienced one in warfare. He was a scribe and recorded all the events that happened. He used this information to advise and predict whether something would work or not. He used all the data that he had collected over the past to counsel Heru's Army. He was very skillful at processing information to make informed decisions.

8. Ka helped people express their unique personality and talents. She made sure that every person in the Army used their gifts to their fullest potential and contributed to the whole. She used her power to tap into the talents of all the Neteru and thus was able to act as a conduit for them to advise Heru and his Army as well. Basically, Ka was like a medium. She could channel any of the Neteru through her, acting as some form of a portal, to let them come through with their talent and specific skills. This was her unique ability which she shared with everyone.

9. Ren was skilled at naming things, events and people. He created the names, look and feel of the Army. In this way, there was order, purpose and direction within the Army. Every member of the Army knew their place and could respond to their commands efficiently. His major responsibility was to take care of Army communications. He became Chief Communications Officer.

10. Khaibit was the force that propelled everything to work in unison. She made certain that every person in the Army had enough tasks to work on. Everything in the Army was fluid because of her.

Her major role was to ensure that the army had sufficient fuel to power all the energy requirements. She also worked closely with Shekhem to train the Army in special weapons and tactics.

11. Khab who was sometimes called Khat, was the engineer who ensured that all the physical resources in the Army were sufficient to train, travel and battle with Set. He took care of food, shelter, clothing, transportation and weaponry.

12. Heru met up with his Council of the Nine Souls on a daily basis to strategise and plan the war at hand. His role was to manage the Vision for the Army and ensure that the Council of the Nine Souls were focused, motivated, purified, disciplined and united, in all aspects. They had to work as a unit without any hint of chaos within. He was the Uniter of all the members of the Army. They were one with him and he was one with them, especially Ba, Ab and Ka.

13. Heru knew however that he needed more men to join his army and he was getting irritated by all the naysayers that were preventing some people from enlisting. So he decided to go and consult Akhu.

14. He conferred with him directly, "It vexes me what some of the people say. I'm terribly vexed. What do you think we should do with those that are defying us and our cause?"

15. Akhu responded colourfully, "I know of a sea snake which has a very strange way of attracting its prey. It will lie still at the bottom of the sea as if it is wounded. Then its enemies will approach and taunt it, and yet it will lie very still. And then

its enemies will take little bites of it, and yet it remains still."

16. "So, we will lie still, and let our enemies come to us and nibble. Continue empowering and training those that have joined us thus far." Said Heru.

17. In due time, when people saw the discipline, strength and military precision that the Army had cultivated, many others joined henceforth. Soon, there was a formidable number of participants and the Army grew in strength, courage and wisdom. It worked like clockwork.

18. And Heru was gratified with the overall progress that his Army had made.

19. One day, he went to his Ancestral shrine to contemplate the depth and significance of the war that was ahead of him and said: "Ancestors. I ask you for your guidance. Blessed Mother, come to me with the Neteru's desire for my future. Blessed Father, watch over my relatives in the Duat with a ready sword. Whisper to them that I live only to hold them again, for all else is dust and air. Ancestors, I honour you and will try to live with the dignity that you have taught me." Consequently, that night, his father the King, Ausar came to visit him in a dream.

20. He said to Heru, "My son, I am so proud of you, and the evolution you have made pleases my heart dearly. You must be patient with your training and in time you can challenge Set in battle. I've seen much of the rest of the world. It is brutal and cruel and dark, because of Set's rule. You are the black light. Only you can save Africans. Are you ready to do your duty for Kamit?"

21. The young Heru responded, "Yes, Father. When do you think I can confront Set's forces? I think I am ready now."

22. "Soon and very soon. You are going to taste victory. But you are still not yet ready, my son. You'll have to wait for a sign from the Neteru. That is our way. We read the symbols of nature, the language of the birds and then know when to act. It tells us what time it is? When the Sun is blocked by the Moon, such that you cannot see it in the world, this will be a sign for you to go forth and confront Set. You will be ready then."

23. "That sounds clear enough for me. Will that be next week or next month or next year?" Heru asked earnestly.

24. Ausar smiled and said, "Again, be patient young man. You will see it, and know it, when you are ready. Right now, go back and train deliberately as hard as you can, because Set will be a formidable opponent. But you have everything you need in the Council of the Nine Souls. They will lead you to victory. On the night before you go to war, you must recite Hymn 357. It will give you confidence and I will be there by your side."

25. And just like that, Ausar vanished as quickly as he had appeared, and Heru woke up from the dream, sweating as if he had been running. He contemplated and meditated on what his father had said to him.

26. Many months passed and Heru continued training and preparing for war with his Army. He never again lost patience with himself. He remembered his father's words and used them to motivate and propel himself forward.

27. Then one day, as Heru was training, he saw darkness befall Kamit during the day. The Sun was covered by the Moon as his father had counseled him, in the dream. He read the language of the birds and understood this message clearly.

28. He remembered his father's words. This was the sign that he had been waiting for. That night, he told his Army and Council of the Nine Souls that on the following day, they would march on to Edfu where they would confront Set in battle.

29. The Army was very excited and motivated, and looked forward to finally battle with Set and his Army. They all shouted in unison, "Hrah! Hrah! Hrah!" The overall mood was festive and buoyant.

30. As soon as Heru got to his sleeping quarters, he recalled what his father had instructed him to do regarding the ancient African hymn. And so he took the ancient hymn from the shelf and began to recite it, to cultivate in himself confidence, strength and awaken the Ausar within.

31. "O! Ausar the King, Geb has given you your eyes, that you may be content with the eyes of this Great One in you."

32. "Geb has caused that Heru give them to you, so that you may be pleased with them."

33. "Auset and Nebt-Het have seen and found you, Heru has reassembled you."

34. "Heru has caused Auset and Nebt-Het to protect you, they have given you to Heru and he is pleased with you."

35. "It goes well with Heru in your company in your name of 'Horizon from which Ra goes forth.'"

36. "In your embrace in your name of 'Inmate of the Palace.' You have closed your arms about him, and his bones are in due order, his heart is proud."

37. "O! Ausar the King, mount up to Heru, betake yourself to him, do not be far from him."

38. "Heru has come that he may recognise you."

39. "He has smitten Set for you bound, and you are his fate."

40. "Heru has driven him off for you, for you are greater than he."

41. "He swims bearing you."

42. "He lifts up one who is greater than he in you, and his followers have seen you, that your strength is greater than his, so that they cannot thwart you."

43. "Heru comes and recognises his father in you, you being young in your name of 'Fresh Water.'"

44. "Heru has split open your mouth for you."

45. "O! King, do not languish, do not groan, for Geb has brought Heru to you that he may claim their hearts for you."

46. "He has brought all the Neteru to you at once, and there is none of them who can escape from him."

47. "Heru has protected you, and he will not fail to protect you."

48. "Heru has wrested his Eye from Set and has given it to you, even this, his sweet Eye."

49. "Make it come back to you, assign it to yourself, and may it belong to you."

50. "Auset has reassembled you."

51. "The heart of Heru is glad about you, in this your name of 'Foremost of the Westerners,' and it is Heru who will make good what Set has done to you."

52. Indeed, after he finished reciting the ancient African hymn, he felt confident, strong and brave enough to lead his Army to victory against Set the following day.

53. By this time, all the naysayers had disappeared as Heru had built himself a strong, united and well-resourced Army. It was well-oiled, sharp, nimble and tactically efficient.

54. The next morning, Heru marched to Edfu, and confronted Set and his Army in battle.

55. Heru stood in front of his warriors in full red and white regalia worthy of a King of Kamit. Like a wise King he broke into speech and said: "My name is Heru Nej Atef, Avenger of his Father, son of Ausar and Auset, Commander of the Armies of the North, General of the Divine Legions and Loyal Servant to the TRUE King, Ausar Khenti Amenti! And I will have my vengeance, today, in this life or the next! Are you ready to do your duty for Kamit? Set has been in charge for two millennia, and that is too damn long! It is time to bring him down. He has ruled all over the world with Isfet: chaos, might and evil. He has disrespected our Ancestors, women and children. He has repeatedly dis-honoured the Children of the Sun, and all that is good in this world. He has stolen land, resources and killed the masses, with no remorse or pity. He has never been taken to court for his war crimes. He has built a criminogenic society. His war-mongering way is not our Way of Maat. His way is inferior and is against Neter! We are the Guardians of Maat, and always have been. We must protect and preserve Maat. This is what this War is about. This is what

you are fighting for. He started it, but we are going to end it! Hold the line! Stay with me! Today, some of us will become Ancestors and join our forefathers in the Duat. You will not be forgotten. Our rituals will feed and elevate you in the Duat, to sit next to your beloved King, Ausar. Do not be afraid, but go boldly and proudly into the Duat! Brothers, today, we'll eat, drink and be merry in the Duat!" When he finished his speech they banged their shields together and all shouted in chorus, "Hrah! Hrah! Hrah! Heru! Heru! Heru!"

56. And with those inspiring, encouraging and vibrant words, the warriors boldly marched forward with vigour. They battled with Set's Army for more than seven days, with temporal breaks in between, to recoup, tend to their injuries, and fight again.

57. But after the seventh day, Heru got the upper hand as Set's army was now exhausted and dispirited because they had expected to battle a weak Army from the "young black boy" as they derogatorily referred to him.

58. However, to their bewilderment Heru defeated Set and was unequivocally declared victorious. Set ran away and became a fugitive in Kamit, as he had previously inflicted the same predicament to Queen Auset, Heru's mother.

59. Heru and his Army searched for him relentlessly. The search did not last long, and he was found in the marshes of the Delta eating pig meat, and having shapeshifted to the form of a crocodile to hide himself. When he saw Heru and his Army, he trembled in fear and disbelief.

60. Set, however, did not concede the fight easily. He took the dispute before a court of the Neteru. He

falsely brought a suit against Heru concerning his legitimacy to rule Kamit. He claimed that he was a better ruler, as he was more brutal and stronger physically, than Heru. And claimed that this was the correct and suitable way to rule and govern men and women, in this world. "People are dumb, blind and brute and they only understand and respond to force and brutality not sweet words," he argued.

61. But Heru, with the aid of Tehuti, obtained recognition from the Neteru. Set was tried in the courts of Kamit, and he lost convincingly. Hence he was sentenced to serve Heru in this world, and his father Ausar in the Duat. Once again, Maat triumphed over Isfet.

62. Ba, Heru's second-in-command, exclaimed to Heru, "People should know when they are conquered."

63. Heru retorted, "Would you, Ba? Would I?" And with that the matter was settled.

64. Heru succeeded his father and he was crowned King of Upper and Lower Kamit.

65. From that day onwards, Heru became known as "Heru Neb Taui." Heru, Lord of the Two Lands.

BOOK OF AFRICAN SPIRITUALITY

Book of Shepsu

Chapter 1

CHRONICLES OF ANI: PRAISES TO AUSAR KHENTI AMENTI UN-NEFER

1. The Great African Sage of Kamit, the Ausar Ani, whose word is truth, Maa Kheru, praises Ausar Khenti Amenti Un Nefer, and says: "Hail, my Lord, who does hasten through eternity, whose existence is forever, Lord of Lords, King of Kings, Sovereign, Neter of the Neteru, who live in their shrines."

2. "Make thou for me a seat with those who are in Khert-Neter, who adore the forms of thy Ka, and who traverse millions of millions of years."

3. "May no delay arise for thee in Ta-meri. Let them come to thee, all of them, great as well as small."

4. "May this Neter give the power to enter in and to come forth from Khert-Neter, without repulse, at any door of the Duat, to the Ka of the Ausar Ani, Maa Kheru, whose word is true."

Chapter 2

HOUSE OF SHEPSU

1. The day after tomorrow, early in the morning, Khem-Netert rushed out of bed to start the process of setting up a shrine. The day before, she had gone to see the Priestess of Auset who had advised her on the procedure of setting up a shrine. Her life was not going well at all, and this was because she was not in touch with her African Spirituality (**AS**). Her life had gotten confused by surrounding herself with the Hyksos, the foreigners that had invaded and conquered Kamit. It had been exactly 72 years since they had come with their filth and chaos to this Blessed Land of Kamit.

2. In turn she had lost touch with her African roots. But in doing so, she had become very chaotic. It was as if Set had been unleashed in her life. First, she lost her mother. Then she lost her husband. Over and above that the second wife was fighting with her over her property that she shared with her husband before he passed away. He left her with two children, a boy and a girl, and she was at a loss for support, because she did not know how she was going to support her two children.

All of these events happened to her in a space of three years. It was three years of pandemonium, she would say to herself.

3. Fortunately for her, one of her brothers told her that she should consult the Priestess of Auset, to give her advice on the matter. At first she was very reluctant because she had become engrossed with the culture of the Hyksos, and their alien ways of relating to the spiritual realm. The Hyksos worshipped Set and Apep. They, especially the rulers, even took on names of these Neteru. In this single act, it would spawn and inspire new mass-popular religions that would later consume the world down the line, several millennia henceforth.

4. These new religions would model Neter in the image and likeness of Set, and would also be just as chaotic and vile as the worship of Set and Apep. These new religions would forever wreak havoc in the world and its native peoples. The masses would become blind, dumb and brute as a result of this new religion. They would eternally divide people based on colour, language, culture, gender and spirituality. Consequently, brother would kill brother for land, and sister would kill sister for status. Isfet, and not Maat, would be the order of the day, as introduced by the worship of Set and the Ego, instead of venerating the Ancestors and Neb er Tcher. The Neteru would become ridiculed, as these new religions would promote and enforce such behaviour amongst the people.

5. Nonetheless, due to her dire situation, Khem-Netert decided to listen to her brother and consult the Priestess of Auset. The Priestess told her that she would need to build a shrine which

would act as a portal between this world and the Duat. By doing so, her Ancestors would then be able to communicate with her and advise her through dreams, events and other significators. Opening the connection would allow her to read signs in her daily life and relate them to her Ancestors. It was the African understanding that there are no coincidences in the world, every effect has a cause. Every effect obeys a law, even if that law may not be known at that particular moment. But it is there operating, being controlled by a Neter behind it.

6. She internalised the reality that the shrine was a symbol. The preserving of the shrine was symbolic of preserving, purifying, protecting, cultivating, maintaining and sanctifying that corresponding force within her. On one hand, it will teach her devotion. On the other hand it will paint a concrete image of an abstract principle and force in her being. That force will provide a means of understanding and communication.

7. Khem-Netert was very excited about the prospect of what she was about to commence. It was a journey of reconnecting with her Ancestors again. What she loved about her African culture was what the Priestess of Auset had said to her, "Nothing in the African way of life is ever lost or forgotten or too drastic to be forgiven and rebuilt to the state that it was before the unfortunate event. What I am saying to you is as good as Law, Maat. If you present yourself as humbly as you possibly can to the Ancestors and Neteru they will always forgive you and help you rebuild your life again as new."

8.   After washing and purifying herself with frankincense oil, she put on a clean white dress, as she had been advised the previous night. She then followed exactly the instructions that she had written down from the Priestess of Auset. She remembered what the Priestess had said to her as if she was standing right in front of her, helping her set up the shrine.

9.   "To make the shrine, you should use a clean white cloth. It should be placed either on a table, or a shelf that has been purified with a good pine cleaner or temple bath and spring water. Never place your shrine on the floor. It should be placed inside the house not outside or in the tool-shed. You should adorn the shrine with a white candle, spring water and malachite stone. Place frankincense oil and myrrh oil, and incense which is the same as the oils. The number 11 is their numeral, so you can place 11 white candles if you so desire. Moreover, on the eleventh month of every year, for eleven days, you must pay special attention to the shrine, tend it, clean it, feed it, and prepare special meals for it. Treat that time as sacred days dedicated to the remembrance of the African Ancestors." she said.

10. The Priestess of Auset continued, "In order to empower the shrine, light the white candle on the shrine, and burn the incense. You must sit in front of the shrine in meditation and chant the following heka repeatedly, 'Shepsu Yakhu Ausar Khenti Amentiu'. While chanting, you should visualise Ausar in full regalia, sitting on a throne in the place where the shrine is positioned. Make the image as realistic as you can. Put Ausar in

front of you. Hold this visualization throughout the entire meditation, as you continue to chant to Ausar. You may visualise yourself giving him your Ab, heart, to place on the shrine. You should end the ritual by saying, 'Anetch Hrak Ausar!' These words are empowering in themselves."

11. "You may also place a picture or statue of Ausar on the shrine, and it should be anointed with frankincense or myrrh. Never place a picture of someone that is still alive in the physical body. I recommend, giving the Ancestors food regularly. However, don't ever give them anything that you would not eat. If it is possible, every time that you eat dinner, you should also prepare a plate for the Ancestors, even if it is just a little bit," she went on with her instructions.

12. "Be sure to serve them first, before you serve yourself. Make sure that you keep all of your shrines clean. The totem for the Ancestors is a coconut, in which the eyes and mouth have been poked out, to form a face. The coconut shall serve as your Ancestor totem. Anoint the eyes and mouth of the coconut with frankincense and myrrh. Be sure to drain all of the coconut water out into a glass, and offer it to the Ancestors on the shrine. Place a glass of water on the shrine regularly, and let it evaporate before you replace it. It is symbolic of them drinking it," she emphasised.

13. "The shrine and totem once dedicated and charged become the 'mouth' of the Ancestors. It becomes a portal or gateway, a line of communication, through the use of symbol. Although it is understood to be a symbol, you should treat it as literal. It will make your shrine

that much more powerful. Treat the shrine as if it is the Ancestors," she smiled as if to say, you are going to thank me later for this wisdom.

14. She then taught her how to offer a mouth to the Ancestors through the shrine. She said to Khem-Netert, "To offer a mouth to the Ancestors you must declare, 'I rise out of the egg in the Hidden Land. May be given to me my mouth, may I speak with it before the Great Neter, the Lord of the Duat. May not my hand and arm be repulsed by the Divine Chiefs of any Neter. I am Ausar Lord of Restau. Shareth Ausar Paut Shepsu, Maakheru, with that being who is on top of the steps. I have come at the wish of my heart, from the pool of fire, I have quenched it. Homage to thee, Lord of Radiance, at the head of the Great House, within night and darkness. I have come to you, I am glorious, I am pure, my two hands are behind you, your portion is with your Ancestors. You give to me my mouth that I may speak with it. May I follow my heart at its season of fire and night.'"

15. "Once a mouth has been offered you then need to activate it, by opening it," the Priestess said to Khem-Netert.

16. She continued with the instructions, "Say these words to your shrine, 'Be opened to me my mouth by Ptah, untie the bandages. Be opened to me my mouth by Ptah. Untie the bandages which are upon my mouth by the Neter of my town. Come then Tehuti filled with Hekau. Untie the bandages. Come then Tehuti filled with Hekau. Untie the bandages of Set which restrain my mouth. Driving them away, Temu shoots at those that would bind me with the fetters of Set. Be

opened my mouth, be unclosed my mouth by Shu with his heavenly iron weapon that he opened the mouth of the Neteru with. I am Shekhemet. I sit upon the west side of the Great Heaven. I am the great Sahu among the souls of Anu. In regards to all Hekau and all words spoken against me, these may the Neteru resist them and all the Paut Neteru resist them.'"

17. When Khem-Netert had finished following all the instructions as counselled to her by the Priestess of Auset, she felt revitalised already. Her spirit was at peace and she felt joy at the same time. She knew that something special had just been re-established by her. She was confident that she had done the right thing to revert to her Ancestral ways. It was the only way for Africans to win back what they lost, she thought.

18. That night when she went to bed, she dreamt of her mother and husband. First she saw her mother dressed in a beautiful white dress smiling to her. Her mother told her that everything will be alright. She was in a good space and place, she comforted her. Then her husband came to see her as well, he too was resting in peace, he reassured her. They both encouraged her to continue on her path. It was a path that would lead her to bliss and success with all her endeavours, they soothed her. Then they left her. She woke up in the middle of the night with tears of joy, and then went back to sleep again, peacefully.

19. In her soul, she knew that there were more joyful encounters to come.

Chapter 3

THE GREAT WARNING

1. The Greatest of the Greatest Sages that ever walked the earth, or any other earth on all the multiverses that bubbled up from Nu, went through his nightly ritual before going to bed to sleep. Imhotep, the wise African, drank his jasmine tea that was prepared by his charming and sweet African wife. It was exactly an hour before he was about to perform his nightly devotional meditation to Ausar which he would start at exactly 9:00 on the dot.

2. He was a stickler for time and accuracy. His modus operandi was, "the relentless pursuit for perfection." At 9:00, the Sage of all Sages, rubbed frankincense oil mixed with spring water on his firm and beautiful black skin. All of this was done after he had taken his fourth bath for the day. After every three hours or so he would stop whatever he was doing, wherever he was engaged, to take a bath. He was strict about cleanliness as were all the Priests of the Nile.

3. It is said that people from all over the world thought of the Kamityu as Neteru. They were the closest that you could get to seeing the Neteru in

the flesh. Some foreigners even wanted to worship the Kamityu for they were so exacting in their way of life which was grounded in Maat.

4.   This was a time when the Children of the Sun, Africans, were the source and spring-water of Light, wisdom, power and civilisation, in the world.

5.   But out of all of the Priests of the Nile, Imhotep stood above all of them. He was said to have become the embodiment of the Neter Ptah. Many were convinced that he had become One with Ptah. The Ka of Ptah had literally fused with the Ka of Imhotep. That way Ptah, the Grand Architect, expressed himself through Imhotep.

6.   With that crystallisation of Ptah, came the many talents that Imhotep possessed. Not only was he surgeon, he was also an engineer. Not only was he an architect but he was also a linguist. Not only was he a priest but he was also vizier to the King. Not only was he a great scribe but he was also a master strategist. And so his many talents and great titles went on and on.

7.   He was unmatched by any mortal in any universe, to say the least. Imhotep always humbly smiled when people bowed down to him in reverence whenever he was in their presence. They simply adored him. But he was a very respectful man. In fact, later on in history, the Children of the Moon, foreigners with no Light of their own, who invaded and annexed Kamit to stay, would worship Imhotep as a "God," in fullness of whatever that word means to the Children of the Moon.

8. After performing the Ausar devotional meditation he went to sleep. That night, in a dream, he was visited by the Great Neter and Founding Ancestor, Ausar Khenti Amentiu.

9. Imhotep's dreams were always lucid. In fact for him he experienced his dreams as if he was awake during the day. It was as if the two realms, Ta and the Duat, had morphed into one, for him.

10. Ausar Khenti Amentiu came in the form of a Golden Falcon wearing the Atef Crown and stood next to him. Imhotep recognised who it was immediately and welcomed the Great Neter and Founding Ancestor.

11. After exchanging pleasantries, Ausar Khenti Amentiu wasted no time and broke into what he had come to convey to the Great Sage of all Sages. The African Extraordinaire.

12. He said, "Do you know, Imhotep, that Kamit is an image of the Duat. In Kamit all the Neteru which operate in the Duat are present in the Earth below? The spirit of Maat dwells and moves in this great land of Kamit."

13. "And yet, since it is fitting that wise men come to pass, you must not be left in ignorance of what I will now tell you."

14. Imhotep was now very curious as to what the Great Neter and Founding Ancestor was about to say and urged him kindly to speak on.

15. And so Ausar Khenti Amentiu continued, "There will come a time when it will have been in vain that the Kamityu venerated Neter and the Neteru with devoted service. All the honour and veneration will be futile."

16. "The Neteru will return to the Duat, Kamit and Africa will be abandoned, and the land which was once the home of Ancestral Veneration will be void of its Great Traditions which took thousands of years to build and evolve."

17. Imhotep was clearly startled and unnerved by what Ausar Khenti Amentiu was saying, but kept silent and listened attentively.

18. Ausar Khenti Amentiu carried on, "O Kamit, O Kamit, O Kamit! Of thy spirituality, nothing will remain but an empty tale, which your own future black children, in time to come will not believe. They will not believe that it was them who built and founded this great wisdom and civilisation. Nothing will be left but words, and only the stones will tell of your greatness."

19. "And in that day men will be weary of life, and they will cease to think of Nature as worthy of reverent wonder. But instead they will be obsessed with their Egos. They will literally worship themselves and personify the Ego as the Creator. Set will be the preferred Neter, and he will replace Ra the Father of the Neteru, as the Creator, for many millennia to come, with his violence, warmongering, and land-thieving tendencies."

20. "Mankind will no longer love this world around us. They will also no longer love their fellow brothers and sisters of the human family. Isfet, chaos, will be the preferred ruler of the land."

21. Imhotep was now disheartened by what Ausar Khenti Amentiu was narrating to him, and he knew that the Great Neter and Founding Ancestor made no mistakes. The Great Neter and Founding Ancestor also rarely visited the Earthly

Realm, Ta. It was only on important matters that he would emerge from the Duat. Clearly, this was one of them, and he had to deliver this message in person.

22. Ausar Khenti Amentiu continued, "Lies will be preferred to Truth. The followers of Set will become heroes, respected and honoured among mankind. Statues will be made of dictators and warmongering generals, which will be worshipped as great, by the Children of the Moon."

23. "Spirituality will be separated from everyday life and be left to one day of the week. The warmongers, mass-genocidal nations, the Children of the Moon, will be celebrated as noble and sophisticated. They will steal land without compensation, all around the world. They will use might to play tricks on their fellow brothers and sisters. Weaponry will be regarded as true civilisation, and the Children of the Moon will be revered for bringing this scourge and terrorism to Africa and other parts of the world. Again, this chaos, too, will be celebrated as valour, strength, courage and honour."

24. "Those who tell the truth will be seen as negative and crazy people, and thus be ostracised. The forked-tongue types and tricksters will rule all nations. Trickery and might will be the order of the day. False History will be enacted to replace True History, as history is written by the victors. The wounded and wronged will not be allowed to tell their history and stories. They will be told to get over it and forget. The Children of the Moon will wipe the Children of the Sun out of the history books. They will turn you into a

people without history with a heathen culture to be rebuked, laughed at and ridiculed."

25. "Unfortunately, most of the Children of the Sun will fall for these tricks and worship the Ego of the Children of the Moon, as 'God'."

26. "Fairy tales will replace Truth and oppose scientific knowledge. The age of the world will be shrunk to several millennia. Set and Apep will be credited with creating the world."

27. "Ancestral and Neteru veneration will become ridiculed by all. They will be seen as primitive and backwards. All knowledge and wisdom which I have given to the world will be corrupted, and some buried and forgotten. My African children, your bloodline, will become servants with no requital. They will be told to forget and forgive. Yet there is no forgiveness without justice, never. They will be denied of their Great Heritage of Kamit. They will be scattered all over the continent southwards, westwards and eastwards due to the invasion of warmongering foreigners. Might will rule over Right."

28. Imhotep interjected, as if to say he had heard enough. He asked Ausar Khenti Amentiu, "I am at a loss for words. How long will this terror and evil last for?"

29. Ausar Khenti Amentiu responded, "It will last until the time when your African bloodline returns to the Way of Kamit. The Way of Maat."

30. "When your African children abandon these foreign religions and revert to African Spirituality (**AS**), History, Traditions and Culture, then the chaos and evil will come to pass."

31. "When your African children say, 'enough is enough,' and return to Ancestral veneration, Neteru cultivation, which is the Way of Maat, then all good things will return to the motherland. Again, the motherland will teach and gift the world true civilisation."

32. "When your African children realise that there is no one or nothing to save them, but themselves, then they will realise the New Vision. Super Africans will emerge."

33. "The New Vision will unfold. They will rise and rise again, like the Benu bird from the ashes, only to evolve and become stronger."

34. "Verily, verily, verily, I say to you, they will grow higher and higher, to teach themselves and the world again. But this is left unto them to decide, for Ra, the Father of the Neteru is Neutral."

35. Again Imhotep interrupted the Great Neter and Founding Ancestor, "Surely there must be something we can do to prevent this time of great strife from coming into being? With all this wisdom and power, surely, there must be something we can do now to prepare for then."

36. Ausar Khenti Amentiu responded, "It cannot be stopped. But it shall come to pass. Life unfolds in cycles. A word of caution, to execute the Resurrection of the Children of the Sun, the Children of Kamit, which will be scattered all over Africa, and abroad in later centuries, you must build Houses of Eternity, Pyramids and Temples. These will preserve the knowledge, wisdom, power and proof of African genius."

37. "Your future bloodline will be able to recognise these teachings, embrace them and decode them

for themselves and the world. They will be the only ones who will be able to decode the wisdom, for the foreigners, the Children of the Moon, will be blinded by their arrogance and Ego."

38. When Ausar Khenti Amentiu, the Great Neter and Founding Ancestor, finished his poignant oracular message, Imhotep said, "Tua Neter. Tua Shepsu. Tua Ausar Khenti Amentiu. Anetch Hrak!"

39. Then Ausar Khenti Amentiu flew away and vanished, as mysteriously and as quickly as he had appeared in the form of the Golden Falcon wearing the Atef Crown.

40. Imhotep immediately awoke, and felt this great pain in his chest, as if his heart was going to implode. He was crying for Africa and her children, the Children of the Sun, because of the "Great Period of Sorrow" that was to come for the Great Black Nations.

41. When the pain had subsided, he knew exactly what he needed to do and started to work on his Pyramid Project and Temple Project. He designed blueprints which would serve as Houses of Eternity that would preserve all the knowledge, wisdom and power of Kamit, for the future generations to be resurrected like the Great Resurrection of Ausar after he was killed by Set.

42. So it was, that the Great Warning was delivered and heeded, and came to be as it was exactly laid out. And the Children of the Sun were left poor, scattered and disunited across the Earthly Realm, Ta. But eventually they slowly prepared for the Second Resurrection of Ausar, by gathering all the members, the wisdom and power together. Slow

and steady, they prepared, again and again, and waited for the right time, to rise and rise again, until lambs become lions.

Chapter 4

THE QUEEN WHO BECAME KING

1. "I am going to create a Great Queen who will rule the world as King. I will bestow upon her many blessings. She will be wise, strong and courageous amongst all men, women and living things. She will be like my own daughter the Netert Het Heru. I think it is about time that I do that. I will be very pleased." Amen-Ra said to the Council of the Neteru that had gathered in front of him.

2. The Neteru were all surprised at what the Father of the Neteru, The Creator of all Things that are and are not, the Bringer of all Forms into being, both seen and unseen. But this too made them very pleased and they offered their help to make it happen.

3. First to speak were Auset and Het Heru who offered their Hekau and said, "Our Father who art in the Duat, we offer all our Hekau in your service and we will do whatever needs to be done in order to make this a reality on Earth."

4. Then Tehuti and Maat spoke and said they had a plan, "We have devised a plan on how to make

this happen, without violating the balance and harmony that is found in the land of Kamit. There exists a noble and deserving Queen by the name of Ahmes. The two Netertu Auset and Het-Heru can use their Hekau on her and bring this Divine Child to be."

5. Amen-Ra then looked at Khnum. "Fashion for me the body of my daughter and the body of her ka," said Amen-Ra, "A great queen shall I make of her, and honour and power shall be worthy of her dignity and glory."

6. "O Amen-Ra," answered Khnum, "It shall be done as you have said. The beauty of your daughter shall surpass that of the Neteru and shall be worthy of her dignity and glory."

7. So Khnum fashioned the body of Amen-Ra's daughter and the body of her ka, the two forms exactly alike and more beautiful than the daughters of men. He fashioned them of clay with the air of his potter's wheel and Heqet, Netert of birth, knelt by his side holding the sign of life towards the clay that the limbs of Amen-Ra's daughter and her ka might be filled with the breath of life.

8. With the help of the two Netertu and their Hekau, Amen-Ra took the form of the noble King Tuthmose and found the Queen, Ahmes, sleeping in her room. When the pleasant odours that proceeded from him announced his presence she woke up. He gave her his heart and showed himself in his Neter-like splendour.

9. When he approached the Queen, she wept for joy at his strength and beauty and he gave her his love.

10. After nine months, the Queen gave birth to a lovely beautiful black daughter, which she named

Hatshepsut, for she knew that this baby was a child of destiny, and was going to do great things.

11. Growing up, Hatshepsut showed great skill in all the tasks she was given which made her father proud. She was good at all her subjects, grammar, rhetoric, arithmetic, dialectic, music, astronomy and geometry.

12. Moreover, Hatshepsut was also great at military strategy, archery, architecture and engineering.

13. What made her father even more honoured by his daughter's achievements was that she competed with everyone to be at the top, both males and females. She was not scared of anyone, lest to say.

14. One day, King Tuthmose declared to his daughter in front of his closest and wisest Council of the Elders, "I will make you to be the first of all living creatures, you will rise as King of Upper and of Lower Kamit, as your father Amen-Ra, who loves you, did ordain."

15. He continued, "This daughter of mine, Khnumet-Amen-Hatshepsut, may she live eternally! I have appointed as my successor upon my throne. She shall direct the people in every sphere of the palace. It is she indeed who shall lead you. Obey her words, unite yourselves at her command."

16. The royal nobles, the dignitaries, and the leaders of the people heard this proclamation of the promotion of his daughter, the King of Upper and Lower Kamit had spoken.

17. This startled all who were there, but they vowed to obey the King's wishes as it was customary to do so in Kamit. Even though this was very unusual, it came to be expected when the King's time came for him to travel to the Duat, and take his place as an Ancestor.

18. After her father's death, 12-year-old Hatshepsut became Queen of Kamit. However, seven years later, when she was of age, Hatshepsut took the unprecedented step of assuming the title and full powers of a King herself as it had been proclaimed by her father.

19. Knowing that her appointment as King of both Upper and Lower Kamit was still highly controversial to some, Hatshepsut fought to defend its legitimacy.

20. She pointed to her royal lineage and claimed that her father had appointed her his successor. She sought to reinvent her image, and in statues and paintings, she ordered that she be portrayed as a male King, with a beard and large muscles.

21. In other images, however, she appeared in traditional female regalia. Hatshepsut surrounded herself with supporters in key positions in government, including Senenmut, her chief minister.

22. She gradually took on the new role, rather than appearing all at once as the King. That would have been a drastic step and so she was rather cautious. She dropped her titles relating to those that only a woman could hold, and took on those of the King.

23. She slowly started the trend towards appearing like a male, wearing the shendyt kilt, Nemes headdress with its uraeus, khat head cloth and false beard.

24. She even, eventually, dropped the female ending from her name. She dropped the "t" and became His Majesty, Hatshepsu.

25. As King, Hatshepsut decided to use the skills that she had learned when she was growing up. She undertook ambitious building projects, particularly around Thebes.

26. She was to prove her might and capability for all to see eternally, so she built an enormous memorial Temple called Djeser-Djeseru, the most sacred of sacred places. It had three colonnaded terraces leading to a sanctuary. She wanted her future African children, and future generations of Africans, to consider it one of the architectural wonders of ancient Kamit.

27. At the temple complex of Karnak, she erected a series of obelisks and built a place for the Netert Maat, a rectangular structure that was composed of a series of small rooms with a large central hall for the placement of the central bark, a small ceremonial boat. The walls of the place were covered with carved and brightly painted scenes of Hatshepsut.

28. While she took on these great feats at home in Kamit, she also decided to travel to foreign lands to spread her wisdom and prowess.

29. She embarked on a trading expedition that brought back vast riches to Kamit, including ivory, ebony, gold, leopard skins and incense. These were brought back to Kamit from the Ancestral land known as Punt.

30. Hatshepsut found the voyage to Punt to be extremely successful and commanded her builders to inscribe on the walls of Djeser-Djeseru, the words, "Never was brought the like of this for any king who had been since the beginning."

31. She was happy with herself and what she had achieved since the time she took over Kamit. She thought that her father would be proud of her too.

32. After many years had come to pass, the Great Queen, Hatshepsut, who ruled as King as well, was also called upon to join her father King Tuthmose as an Ancestor in the Duat.

33. It is said that the people of Kamit mourned and commemorated their Great Ruler for many moons afterwards.

34. Her many achievements remain for all to see in the great African land of Ancient Kamit.

Chapter 5

INVOCATION OF ANI

1. Nefer Ptah, an Initiate of the Temple of Anu was confounded by a number of questions that were streaming relentlessly in his head. His head was literally spinning with numerous questions. He wanted to know so many things but did not want to ask the Elders or the other High Initiates.

2. He wanted to query the Shepsu themselves. His questions bordered around the essence of Ancestral Veneration and knowing exactly who the Ancestors were and what form they existed in. He had asked his father these questions a long time ago when he was younger, but he was not satisfied with the answers that he received from his father. So he still yearned to know more.

3. He then plotted that he would invoke the Great Ancestor Ani during the Winter Solstice. He did not know how to do it himself but had heard of a book which contained the procedure in the Inner Temple chambers where only the High Initiates were allowed to go.

4. On the first night of the Winter Solstice, he decided to wait for the High Initiates to go to sleep. After everyone was fast asleep, he crept to

the Inner Temple and took the key from where it was hidden. Earlier on he had carefully observed one of the High Initiates to see how they entered the Inner Temple and also where the Book of Hekau was kept.

5. He took the key from its secret compartment and opened the wooden door that led to the Inner Temple. Once inside he rushed to open the shelf that harboured the Book of Hekau. All went according to plan, and he managed to get the book.

6. He opened the Book of Hekau and quickly searched for the chapter that contained the invocation of the Great Ancestor Ani. He read the instructions and then followed them exactly.

7. He chanted, "I am a Divine Lion, coming forth with strides. I have shot forth arrows, I have wounded the prey. I have wounded the prey. I am the Eye of Heru. I have opened the Eye of Heru in his hour. I have come unto the furrows. Let Ausar Ani come in Peace."

8. As he chanted this invocation, he visualised the Great Ancestor Ani standing before the Inner Temple door with a staff in his left hand.

9. After about seven minutes, the Ka of the Great Ancestor Ani appeared in front of him. Nefer Ptah was shaken by the efficacy of the invocation. He thought to himself, "It worked." Then he calmed himself down and regained composure. The Great Ancestor Ani was dressed in sparkling white attire. His black skin appeared supple and healthy as a baby's skin, and his black beard was well groomed. His brown eyes were full of wisdom, thought Nefer Ptah.

10. The Great Ancestor Ani asked him, "My son why have you called me from this deep sleep?"

11. Nefer Ptah responded, "Anetch Hrak Ani! I am sorry to disturb your peaceful sleep. I have been sleeping sparingly myself, for the past few days, and it is because I have some questions which I fear no man can answer but you."

12. Ani replied, "What is it that I may do for you? Our Ancestors created this technology of Ancestral communication for exactly this purpose so that we can counsel the young, in times of need. I am happy to help you with your questions."

13. Nefer Ptah, now at ease, started with shooting his questions, "Please teach me everything you can about the Ancestors. Who are the Ancestors? Why do we as Africans venerate them? Are there levels, as in a hierarchy, of Ancestors? How does it all work? Please teach me, I will just shut up and listen."

14. Ani smiled and was encouraged by the fire and eagerness that was in the young Initiate's spirit. He said, "Okay, I will teach you as much as I can with the time that I have. You can interrupt me anytime to get more clarification with some of the answers."

15. Nefer Ptah said excitedly, "We have an understanding then, you may begin."

16. Ani then went on a long monologue, as if he was teaching his own son.

17. "The Neteru, represent our spiritual Ancestors. These are the forces that our bodies descended from. At the highest level of our being, you are

the creator of the Neteru, yet as an Individuated Person, you are a descendant of them."

18. Nefer Ptah interjected, "Why are you starting with the Neteru, I am particularly interested in the Ancestors."

19. "Patient young soul, all in good time, you have to understand the whole being first, before we touch on the Ancestors," Ani smiled and then continued.

20. "The Neteru make us up, and they make up every facet of life. Our bodies are the culminations of their creative process, and consist of them in the same way that we descend from our physical Ancestors. We are a culmination of the Ancestors, chemically and biologically. Everything that makes us up physically, we received from our mother and father, our Ancestors, even our breathing in the womb."

21. "The mother and father principle that brings life into being at the highest level, as the Creator comes into being, also operates and creates on the physical level. This was understood by Africans, and this is why family and Ancestral Veneration was the order of the day."

22. "Neter is Nature! The Creation that happens between a man and a woman on every level is Neter."

23. "Traditionally we, as Africans, elevated our Ancestors. We elevated our Elders. We elevated our mother and father."

24. "They were elevated because we descended from them, they were our physical creators. Our physical and chemical make-up is inherited from them. We elevated the Ancestors, based upon the level of their experience and wisdom."

25. Nefer Ptah spoke again and said, "Thank you, please continue, I am loving this very much. This is exactly what's been troubling me, I want to know more."

26. Ani retorted, "I know. I know. I know exactly what's on your mind, young soul. Let me proceed with the teachings. There are different levels of Awareness. People are not on the same level as a whole, on earth and also in the Duat. We vary based upon our level of Awareness and our experience."

27. "The higher the level of Awareness, the higher one sits on the 'Tree of Life.' There is a hierarchy to life. This hierarchy manifests itself in Nature as well, at every level. Our traditional households, communities and cultures were founded upon this hierarchy. Elders held a high rank because of their wisdom and experience."

28. "The African Elders were walking libraries and Oracles. They were the keepers of the African traditions. They were considered close to the Ancestors, due to their age, and the reality that they too would soon become Ancestors. I must add that in regards to the hierarchy, it also exists among the Ancestors."

29. Nefer Ptah asked again, "What is the hierarchy of Ancestors? That sounds very interesting. It makes so much sense though."

30. Ani replied, "The hierarchy of Ancestors is Shepsu, Yakhu, and Ausar Khenti Amentiu."

31. "All Ancestors have the potential to be a Sheps. This word, Sheps, means honourable, or noble. Some Shepsu gained this status automatically, as they lived a life of Maat, though they may not have attained to Self-Realization."

32. "Being righteous was an automatic ticket to becoming a Sheps. Other Ancestors may not be on that level from the start, but can be elevated to the level of a Sheps. Life is a circle, not a line. Our Journey continues even as we transcend this side of Life."

33. "Kamit depicts the circle of life beautifully, as Ra's travels from the East, as birth, and to the West, as death. The Sun rises in the East and sets in the Beautiful West."

34. "As Ra enters the West he journeys through the Duat, and eventually is reborn in the East. In a sense, when we are born into this world, we die in the Duat, and when we die in this World, we are born into the Duat."

35. "The Journey continues! Experience continues, evolution continues!"

36. "Therefore, when a person leaves this side of life, even though they may not have lived a life that automatically qualifies them for Sheps status, through the proper rituals, and service, their Ka could be purified and elevated to the level of a Sheps."

37. "In fact by being enshrined, they could continue to serve and work in the Duat, in the community, in the family, continuing their journey, continuing their evolution."

38. "We, as Africans, have rituals designed to elevate the Ka of an Ancestor to the level of a Neter. There are rituals that assist in restoring the consciousness to the Ancestor, and setting up a system of service for their Ka."

39. Nefer Ptah then asked another question, "Sheps Ani can you tell me more about the Ka? We are

learning a lot about it here but I would like to hear your guidance on it."

40. "The Ka is the aspect of our Being that gives us our unique expression and personality."

41. "The Ka also houses the information that we accumulate on our journey."

42. "The Ka continues its own individual existence, even though the Ba, soul, may reincarnate."

43. "Before you ask me about the Ba, let me describe it to you. The Ba, soul, is the body that houses our Individuated Akhu and Shekhem. The Akhu is Universal Intelligence, and the Shekhem is Universal Energy. The Ba is considered Heavenly, while the Ka is considered Earthly."

44. "Anyway, the Ka continues its existence in the Duat, or may take up residence in the tomb that houses its body, Khat. It is especially true, if the tomb serves also as a shrine for it to receive offerings, and also communicate with its descendants."

45. "The Ka must be fed, just as the body, Khat, must be fed. Think about when you are hungry. Imagine if you were starving, you would be scrounging around for food, and begging for food."

46. "At worst, you would get to a low point, where you may even have to steal food. This is actually the reality of what most 'Dark Spirits' are. They are not bad people per se, but these are starving Kau!"

47. "A 'Dark Spirit' is a Ka that is starving, because the family or descendants have abandoned their culture of Ancestral Veneration. However, it can be elevated to become a Sheps."

48. "Traditionally, we understood that the Kau of our Ancestors need to be fed, and this is why we set in place systems of Ancestral Service."

49. "We perform Ancestral Service to make sure that our Ancestors are healthy and strong enough to continue their existence on the other side of life in the Duat."

50. "We want our Ancestors to enjoy themselves, so that they may continue to play an important part in our life, the family, and the community."

51. "What do unhappy family members do? They create friction and disharmony. If you are in a position to help them, you can end their dissatisfaction and starvation, and elevate them to a better condition."

52. "Most 'Dark Spirits' are hungry Kau that have become parasitic because no one is feeding their Ka, and as a result they are dissatisfied and create disharmony."

53. "The next level of the Ancestors are the Yakhu. Yakh means light or star. These are Enlightened Ancestors, Shepsu that have Realised Self. Even though all of them are Enlightened, among them there is still a hierarchy based upon seniority, how old the Sheps is, and how much experience he or she has."

54. "Next in line at the top of the hierarchy is Ausar Khenti Amentiu. Ausar, which is more correctly Aus-Ir, means place or Seat of the Eye."

55. "Khenti Amentiu means Chief, First, or Head of those in Amenta or the Duat."

56. "Ausar Khenti Amentiu is a title of the Oldest and Wisest Sheps of them all. He or She sits upon the throne among the Paut Shepsu. Understand

that all the Ancestors collectively are The Paut Shepsu."

57. "The hierarchy determines the position that the Ancestors hold in the Duat."

58. "Ausar Khenti Amentiu sits as the Head of the Paut."

59. "Ausar Khenti Amentiu makes decrees from the throne. The rest of the hierarchy carries out the decree. The orders given are based upon the time, and what must be done. They are based on what is in the best interest of the whole family. This exists on a collective scale as it relates to the Family of Mankind, and also on a personal scale for each family."

60. "You, Nefer Ptah, came into being by decree from your Shepsu, through your ancestral line to serve as the Heru to restore Maat in your bloodline."

61. "The Ancestors work for Neter in the Duat."

62. "We are doing the work on this side of life, and they are doing the same on the other side of life."

63. "Just as we elevate them by doing the work on this side, on earth, they also elevate us by doing the work on that side in the Duat."

64. "Some Ancestors work for other Ancestors, they are employees. In all cases, if the work is done, if rituals are done, if the Kau are fed, the Shepsu can be elevated to Yakhu status."

65. "Since the Ancestors are men and women, they are Neter incarnate. They have the potential to gain mastery over their Being, over the Neteru, and exercise influence in the world through the power of the spirit. They can embody the Neteru incarnate."

66. "You must venerate the Ancestors, and elevate their Kau. This is not to say worship them. You

are also a Neter that's still learning about itself. The circle is one."

67. "You must recognise their seniority, their wisdom, and their experience. You must respect them just as you do your parent. You must honour them."

68. "You must take care of the Ancestors and they will take care of you because that's what family is supposed to do, for each other."

69. "I said to you that Yakh means light or Star. The Africans teach that great people, wise people, become stars, or light beings. These stars serve as guides on our journey as we grow to become stars ourselves."

70. "My young soul, I trust this answers most of your questions, I must go in peace now. It is time."

71. Nefer Ptah was overwhelmed by all this wisdom and wanted to ask some more questions but did not even know where to start. He also realised that it was now very late and anytime now he would be caught in the Inner Temple and that would bring about some unwanted consequences. He thanked the Great Ancestor and said, "Tua Neter, Tua Shepsu. Anetch Hrak Ani! Hetepu!"

72. Ani the Great Ancestor left and reverted to the Duat. Nefer Ptah made sure that the Inner Temple looked as if no one had intruded into it. He went back to his room. Though he had done a most foolish thing by creeping into the Inner Temple, he knew that he had gained a lot, and grown a lot, just by that conversation he had with the Great Ancestor Ani. He was elated.

73. He thanked his Ancestors and Neter, again, and then slept peacefully, for the first time in a long time.

Chapter 6

BOOK OF MAKING
THE SPIRIT OF AUSAR

1. During the Heb Nen, the Festival of Surrendering, which happens every Winter Solstice, a young and graceful black woman of Kamit, by the name of Akhu, recites the Book of Making the Spirit of Ausar. The Book is known to energise and enliven the Ba of the person who recites it during the Heb Nen, and also at other times throughout the year.

2. She bows down and then begins to recite the Book in earnest, and says:

3. Come to thy house, come to thy house, O An. Come to thy house, O beautiful Bull, the Lord of men and women, the beloved one, the lord of women. O Beautiful face, Khenti of Akertet, Prince, First of those who are in the Duat, are not all hearts drunk through love of thee, O Un Nefer, MaaKheru?

4. The hands of men and Neteru are lifted on high seeking for thee, even as those of a child are stretched out after his mother. Come thou to them, for their hearts are sad, and make them to appear as beings who rejoice. The lands of Heru

exult, the domains of Set are overthrown through fear of thee.

5. Hail Ausar, first of those who are in the Duat! I am thy sister Auset. No Neter hath done for thee what I have done for thee, and no Netert. I made a man child though I was a woman, because of my desire to make thy name live upon the earth. Thy divine essence was in my body. I placed him on the back of the earth, I brought him forth. He pleaded thy case, he healed thy suffering, he decreed the destruction of him that had caused it. Set hath fallen before his sword, and the Smamiu fiends of Set have followed him. The throne of Geb is to thee, O thou who art his beloved son!

6. Hail Seker-Ausar! This calamity happened to thee in the primeval time. There have been made for thee, mighty chambers in Tchettu. The Neter Utekh embalmed thee and made sweet the smell of thee. The Neter Anpu toiled for thee in the place of purification, and performed all the things which he had to perform. I and my Sister Nebt-Het kindled a lamp at the door of the Arit chamber, so that we may snare Set in a net, like a goose.

7. Anpu came forth from the place of purification and overthrew all thine enemies. The mourners, male and female, made for thee lamentations. Heru hath overthrown the Sebau, and hath cast fetters about Set.

8. The Neteru stand up and utter groans by reason of the great calamity which hath happened to thee, and they send forth their loud cries unto Heaven. Those who dwell in the horizon hear the Netert making lamentation over the motionless

one, they see what the accursed one hath done to thee.

9.   Tehuti stands at the door of the pure chamber in order to recite his formula which shall give life to the Ba each day. The ploughing of the earth hath been performed for thee in the season of Akhet. Thou comes forth in the Duat.

10.   The sons of Heru are with thee. Heru is before thee with rope in his hands. The Neter Atef and Neter Hem prepare thy two ways in the pure chamber. Thy mouth is opened by the Opening of the Mouth.

11.   The Kheri Heb and the Khenti of Uabu with their books of making the Ba to live in their hands, recite the formula over thee. The Ashem hath opened thy mouth. Seker in the Hennu Boat hath triumphed, thine enemies are overthrown.

12.   Hail Ausar Khenti Amenta. Come to thy sister O Un Nefer, Maakheru, come to thy Wife!

13.   Hail Ausar Khenti Amenta, the Neteru with their heads on their knees, await thy coming to them, men with outcry and shouting call out: 'O Ba, perfect to all eternity, thy members are in a state of well being, thy sufferings are relieved, every evil thing in thee is done away. Thy limbs are rejoined, thou art protected, thou hast no defect. Thy limbs are rejoined, and not a member of thine is wanting.'

14.   Hail Ausar Khenti Amenta! O form, thou hast thy head, O Neter of the lifted hand, thy crown and thy hair are made of genuine lapis lazuli.

15.   Hail Ausar Khenti Amenta! O form, thou hast thy two eyes, thou sees with them. The Maati Netert love to protect thee.

16. Hail Ausar Khenti Amenta! O form, thou hast thine ears, wherewith thou shalt hear prayers for millions of years.

17. Hail Ausar Khenti Amenta! O form, thou hast thy nose, thy nostrils snuff the breezes.

18. Hail Ausar Khenti Amenta! O form, thou hast thy mouth, thou speaks therewith, Heru has pressed for thee thy mouth.

19. Hail Ausar Khenti Amenta! O form, thy jaw bones are on thee, firmly fixed.

20. Hail Ausar Khenti Amenta! O form, thy beard is made of crystal which emits rays of light.

21. Hail Ausar Khenti Amenta! O form, thy lips are flint and thy teeth are turquoise.

22. Hail Ausar Khenti Amenta! O form, thy tongue is the pilot of the Two Lands, it licks up thine enemies.

23. Hail Ausar Khenti Amenta! O form, thy body is Natron, it perishes not.

24. Hail Ausar Khenti Amenta! O form, neck bears ornaments and amulets which reach to thy throat.

25. Hail Ausar Khenti Amenta! O form, thy hands are firm on the staff, which is stable in thy abodes.

26. Hail Ausar Khenti Amenta! O form, thy sinew and thy vertebrae are established firmly.

27. Hail Ausar Khenti Amenta! O form, thy belly, thy secret place, hides that which is in it.

28. Hail Ausar Khenti Amenta! O form, thy two shoulders are established firmly on thy back.

29. Hail Ausar Khenti Amenta! O form, thou hast thy member and thy genitals that thou may copulate.

30. Hail Ausar Khenti Amenta! O form, thou hast thy backbone and thy buttocks, thou sits upon the throne every day.

31. Hail Ausar Khenti Amenta! O form, the soles of thy feet are on the earth, the water flood appears with them, O Ausar Khenti Amenta!

32. Hail Ausar Khenti Amenta! Auset and Nebt-Het say: 'Thou hast received thy head, thou hast united in. Thy embrace thy flesh, thy limbs thou hast brought unto thyself. Thou hast gathered together thy members, and they have come into thy mummified form. Thou hast become like the Neter Sebek, the Neb of the Khat.'

33. Hail Ausar Khenti Amenta! There is health in thy members, thy wounds are done away, thy suffering is relieved, thy groaning shall never return. Come to us, thy sisters, come to us. Our hearts will live when thou comes. Men shall cry out to thee, women weep for thee with gladness at thy coming to them. The Two Lands shall not lack thy name, and thou shalt be established in the nomes of the Neteru for ever.

34. Hail Ausar Khenti Amenta! Rise up, rise up! Be thou not motionless. Thy son Heru overthrows thine enemies.

35. Rise thou up into heaven, unite thy self to Ra. The mariners of the Divine Boat ascribe praises unto thee. The mouths of the Neteru of the horizon utter glad words.

36. Throats follow thee, thy love is in their hearts, thy terror is in their breast, when thou enters into the Utchat, and unites thyself thereto.

37. Those who are on the earth and those who are in the Duat flourish. O Bull, who renews youth in the sky each day, creator of the Great Paut Neteru.

38. At thy entrance into the Utchat, the Shekhem of Ausar, that is to say, Tehuti, cometh into being.

39. When thou rises in the sky calamity departs, and when thou art seen in the sky on this day, bulls fecundate the cows and very many conceptions take place.

40. Hail Ausar Khenti Amenta! Thou becomes a child in the horizon of heaven each day, and thou becomes old at every one of thy periods.

41. Hapi appears by the command of thy mouth, making men and women to live on the effluxes which come from thy members, making every field to flourish. At thy coming, that which is motionless grows, and the green plants of the marsh put forth blossoms.

42. Hail Ausar Khenti Amenta! Thou art Lord of a million years, the lifter up of the wild animals, the Lord of cattle, every created thing hath its existence from thee. To thee belongs what is in the earth, to thee belongs what is in the waters, to thee belongs whatsoever is in them in thy name of Hapi.

43. Hail to thee, in thy name Inert One, Khenti Het Urit. Thou art the Lord of Truth, the hater of sinners, who makest them to be overthrown in their sins.

44. The two Maati Netert are with thee, on no day do they depart from thee. Sins cannot draw nigh unto thee in any place wherein thou art. To thee belongs whatsoever appertains to life and to death. To thee belongs whatsoever appertains to men and women.

45. Hail Ausar Khenti Amenta! The mourners weep, both men and women, and they lament. The Hekau of thy bier protects thee at all seasons,

thy members are guarded. All thine enemies are overthrown.

46. Thy throne is established firmly each day like the throne of Ra, with mighty sovereignty, by ruling to his son's son. Shu and Tefnut were with him in primeval time.

47. Shu says: 'O Son of a son, I am thy son. Thou renews thy youth at the word, it is I who gives air to the throat which is closed, and from it proceeds life to the throat. Thou art sovereign among the Neteru, the prince at the head of the Paut Neteru.'

48. Tefnut says: 'There is love to thy mother who conceived her father, on the day, giving birth to thee with gladness. I made the form of the Ammit to overthrow all thine enemies. Likewise, all which I made for my father Ra in primeval time I have made for Ausar Khenti Amenta, in order to create his form anew. I am the mother of thy mother, I am thy eldest daughter, thou art my Shekhem. Men and women sing hymns of praise when thou rises on us at the season of thy departure. The beings of the South and the beings of North must not be without a sight of thee. The Beings of the West and the Beings of the East are settled in the fear of thee, and they bear tribute on their heads each day. They shall never separate from thy Majesty by reason of their desire to see thee.'

49. Hail Ausar Khenti Amenta! Come to me, I am thy sister Auset. Rise up, rise up, come at my call. Hearken thou to the recital of the things which I have done for thee, which I have done for thee and thy name in all the nomes, and in every domain, and how they hold thee in fear. They cry out unto thee at the time of thy departure. Their hearts are

not wearied because of their love for thee. Be not afar off, come thou to us.

50. Hail Ausar Khenti Amenta! Thy mother Nut gave birth to thee in Thebes, and thou didst become a young man. As soon as thou didst rise on the earth as a child there was a shout of joy, and Ra heard it in his abode in the land of the North, hearts rejoiced at thy birth. Thou arrives at Henensu on the night of the Full Moon. Ra saw thee, thy love entered into his heart in the royal seat. He gave to thee the throne of Geb. Thou art his son whom he loves.

51. Thou enters into the temple, into thy hidden abode, in Het Benben. The Neteru in Aatcha-Mut rejoice at the sight of thee. The city of Menefer is with thee every day and thou lives there in the form of Atem-Khephera, the prince of Anu. Abtu is thy city in the land of the South, thou art there in it every day in the form of Ausar Khenti Amenta, the Great Neter, the Lord of Abtu.

52. Auset stops the paths before that evil one at Abtu, thy son Heru overthrows thine enemies every day. Thou renews thy youth in Djedtu. The Netert Nebt-Het protects thee, the Netert Shenat keeps off the fiend Set. The temple Anti is full of loud acclamations, and Restau is full of splendour.

53. The Neter Khnum protects thee in Metchat. He pours out for thee, water in the Hetep Chamber in the Metchat Temple, appearing in it anew, appearing from thee.

54. The city of Behudet is established under thy name, Heru overthrows Set. The city of Heru of the West rejoices at the sight of thee. The temple of Aptet hath joy of Heart.

55. The Spirits who dwell in Nekhent cry out with Joy. The Netert Nekhebet protects thee in Nekhebet. Splendid is thy rising up as the Lord of the South and North. She is like a vulture in effecting thy protection, and she is like a uraeus established on thy head. She makes thee to rise like Ra every day. Offerings to thee, with joy, with joy.

56. The Neter An purifies thee in Het-Shekhemu. Nifu-Urt rejoices because of thee, thou art on the roads which are in it. The Pauti Neteru exalt thee high on thy standard. The Neteru look upon the two Merti Netert who are before thee. Thy two Uatcheti Netert are in thy following, thou art never deprived of them.

57. The city of Shena-Hennu rejoices at thy Ka, and the cities of Apu and Khent-Menu utter many loud cries of joy. Het-Heru protects thee, thou lives for ever in Hetep.

58. Thou builds up men and women, thou art the guide of Neteru in thy name of Khunm. Thy members are gathered together in Het-Ertuu, and the Neteru who dwell therein overthrow thine enemies.

59. The Neter Tehuti recites the Book of Making the Spirit for thee in Khemenu, and the Eight Neteru of Khemenu ascribe to thee praises as they did for thy father Ra.

60. The Neteru of the city of Hesert rejoice in thee, from the time thou enters till thou departs. Henensu adores thy Ba, and An-aarrut-f is under thee, every day. Mer-Ur rejoices at thy coming. Thou hides thy body in Pa-Hennu until Het-Heru cometh.

61. Men-Nefer is established possessing thee. Kindled for thee is a fire in the hands of the Netert Rerit, she performs acts of protection for thee every day. Ptah gives air to thy nostrils. The Merti Neteru Khentiu of the Temple of Ptah protects thee. The sanctuary of Shetaut rejoices, the Hennu sanctuary is glad. The heart of Ptah-resuaneb-f is glad, he rejoices in thy love.

62. The temple of Sekhet resounds with music in thine honour. The temple of Aqert rejoices possessing thee, and Heru overthrows all thine enemies.

63. The Neteru are full of the sight of Thee. Thou art protected by Nut in the city of the Apis, Menefer rejoices in thine Image. Thou sucks in pure life with the milk of Sekha-Heru, and the town is full of happiness.

64. The Netert Sekhemet protects thee in the lands of the Thehennu, she defends thee, the Queen of Mer-Ur is glad. The Netertu of the Paut Neteru tarries with thy Ren in the temple of Neith, the city is filled with glory at the sight of thee. Thou becomes hidden on the South side and on the North Side, thy apparel is the work of the Two Sebeku. Thou comes, thou passes into the temple of Het Khebit.

65. The Netert Neith shoots arrows from her bow to overthrow thine enemies utterly. Thou reaches and thou appears in the form of the bull upon his stand in thy name of Ausar Ua, whilst Auset stands before thee. She never leaves thee. Thy name is in the mouth of her inhabitants, they praise thee where thou art all day long, even as they praise Ra, the father of thy parents, the throne which thou loves is in her.

66. The Uraei Netertu rejoice in thy image, and their sceptres bring thee healing, season by season. The city of Pe rejoices at the sight of thee, and Tep brings hymns and praises before thy face. The Netert Uatchet, the Uraeus Netert, takes up her place on thy head. Clusters of papyrus plants are presented to thee in the city of Khebit. All thine enemies are overthrown. The city of Qebhher and Nai, bow themselves down before thy face.

67. The children and young men come to thee from Anu. The awe of thee fills the temple of the Neter Sep, and thy name is spread abroad. Kheraha is full of joy at the sight of thee, and the temple of Amahet has gladness of Ba.

68. Shenu-qebh is filled with joy of heart, and the sacred city is glad and under the form of Hetepet, the Netert Het-Heru guards thee. Bast sends awe of thee among all men. Thy strength against thine enemies is great.

69. The Neter Sep, the Heru of the East, the Slayer of the Anti rejoices at the sight of thee. Heru Merti protects thee, and overthrows all thine enemies in the town of Sheten. The town of Tchan is glad, and the land of Haa is full of Joy.

70. The town of Theb-Neter bows low before thee. Heru-Tema, with lofty plumes, the lord of the crown, is the vanquisher of all thy foes.

71. The town of Het-Bau possesses thy Ram, and thou appears as Ba-Neb-Tet, the virile Ram, the master of virgins.

72. Khenemu lies under thy rule, and Tehuti, the judge of the Two Combatants, establishes the writings which commemorate the battle. Thou art in the Place of Ra forever.

Chapter 7

SENEBTY AND THE GIFT OF ANCESTRY

1.   Senebty had just finished signing the last papers which confirmed that she was leaving her second husband, for good. It made her very sad, because this was the second time it was happening to her. She thought this one was going to work because she really loved this man and felt connected to him.

2.   It was as if there was a force in her that did not want her to get married, to be with someone. Senebty did not understand what was happening to her. Nothing seemed to be going her way.

3.   At least she did not have any children from both marriages, she consoled herself. She had seen how it always turned nasty when parents with children separated. She believed that it affected the children, adversely. That is something she did not want to happen or be responsible for. At that age it is difficult for children to understand such matters of the heart.

4.   "Tua Neter. Tua Shepsu," she thought to herself. Senebty was thanking the Ancestors and Neteru

for the fact that Kamit was civilised enough to have laws that allowed the husband and wife to separate permanently. She had heard of faraway lands where this sort of arrangement was not allowed. To her, this was unthinkable, to live with someone who you no longer cared for, or who no longer shared the same vision with you for the future.

5. The only aspect of her life that seemed to be going well was her work, and the love and support that she got from both her parents and siblings.

6. Senebty's work in the Temple of Het Heru at Dendera involved recording all the offerings that were made by the people of Kamit to the Netert. She loved her work as it gave her access to the Library and Sacred Writings of Het Heru. To get to become a scribe, she only had to do the introductory level of Initiation. This stage was more of a purification stage. Once she completed it, she was offered the position at the Temple and she gladly accepted it.

7. Senebty had a dream once in which her Sheps grandmother visited her and said repeatedly, "The Ancestors want you, they have something to give you, and you must accept it without question." The dream had startled her, and she woke up sweating as if she had been running a marathon.

8. But, nonetheless, she chose to ignore the dream as swiftly as it had come. However, with the way everything was going in her life, it was becoming too much to bear and she wanted to get better answers from an expert, who could help her.

9. She was at the crossroad of her life, and she was convinced wholeheartedly, that something different had to be done.

10. She was losing control of her life, more so than before. In fact it was steadily becoming worse.

11. After two failed relationships, she wondered what she was doing wrong. She never wanted to consult the Oracle of Denderra about this to find out the truth.

12. She was always scared of the truth. She thought it would mess up her destiny. She felt that knowing would somehow bring about adverse effects.

13. However, after this failed relationship, she decided to cast all doubts aside and approach the Oracle of Denderra, the famous Hetankhu.

14. Hetankhu could only be consulted in the early hours of the day, at sunrise, and on a sunny, and cloudless day.

15. Senebty went to speak to Hetankhu's assistant and requested an appointment. She could only get a booking in fourteen days' time. Hetankhu was very busy, in fact Senebty was very lucky to even get an opening.

16. It normally took about a month to get a booking for consultation with Hetankhu. That is how popular and proficient she was with her gift of Insight. Her work of Divination involved her uncovering the forces, be it Shepsu or Neteru, that were working behind the event that was troubling the querent. Her specialty was not foretelling the future, even though she could do that and inform the querent about the possibilities inherent in the direction that the querent was taking.

17. She was brilliant at revealing the nature of the Duat with regards to what was occurring on earth. By doing so, the querent would then be advised on what course to take, in order to create harmony

in the Duat. By creating harmony in the Duat, it would result in harmony being effected on earth. "As above, so below" was the High Science being used in such matters, as she liked saying to her clients. Her fame was known worldwide. Kings and Queens, from far and wide, used to visit her every now and then, to consult on various important matters.

18. Hetankhu refrained from foretelling because she found that it usually caused people to slumber into analysis-paralysis. She would only do it if it was another Priestess or Priest requesting her services. But for the average person who was not an Initiate, she would decline to comment. "Great Power in the hands of those that have no Wisdom is a curse." That is what her teacher used to emphasise repeatedly to her. From that advice, she decided that she would treat her gift with special care.

19. After fourteen days, Senebty was seated in front of Hetankhu. "Finally," she thought.

20. "How can I help you?" She asked.

21. "My life is not going well, I think. I have been married twice and the second marriage just ended. I feel as if some force is preventing me from having a permanent partner and happy relationship," Senebty responded.

22. "It seems as if you already have the answers to your question. I do not even have to cast any bones for your question. The force you are talking about is real," she said.

23. "You have an Ancestor in your bloodline, that wants to bestow a Gift upon you. This is the same Gift that I have. This Ancestor is from your

mother's side. She too got it from her grand-parents. The Gift is passed down the bloodline from generation to generation," she continued.

24. "If you accept this Gift you will have the same powers as I have. Maybe even better who knows. But your Ancestor was a very powerful Sage in Ancient Kamit. Even more ancient than Old Kamit. This is your Destiny, Senebty. You cannot run from it. Running from it will only make your life even harder. That is why you have failed in marriage. But not too worry, the Ancestors will find you the right man, once you have accepted the Gift. Nonetheless, we already have the Initiation process well documented that you would have to follow, if you accepted this Gift," she said.

25. "It is a Gift that is given to us by Neter passed on to some blessed and fortunate people. To say the least, you are fortunate to have been selected. Do you know how many people would choose to be in your position?" Said Hetankhu.

26. "Many, I presume," replied Senebty.

27. "Good, then at least you understand and appreciate its importance. The Gift is given to us so that we can help others. There are many lost souls that need our help. We become counsellors to them, we guide them and show them the Way of Maat, if we do it right. We show them the North Star. Yes, some people may abuse the Gift, but those are the exception, not the rule," said Hetankhu.

28. "The first thing you must do is accept the Gift. I will guide you in this process. The second thing is to then go through Initiation. I'm afraid you have no choice in the matter. Or rather you always have a choice but each door you open has its own

consequences, some good, others not-so good. But I'm sure you already know how difficult life can be if you reject the Gift," she said.

29. Senebty interjected, "So it leaves me no choice really, because if I don't accept it, then the consequences are dire! And if I accept it then I will have to live a different life."

30. Hetankhu reassured her, "True. But then this is the life that was scripted for you. Before you came down and reincarnated, you sat down with the Ancestors and agreed a lifepath for yourself, so that you could learn and evolve to a higher level. This is part of it, the Gift that is. You accepted this lifepath in the Duat, you must accept it graciously now on earth, and you will be in harmony with your Destiny. You will be in harmony with the Sekher Neter, the Divine Plan. The African Way is a life of order and harmony. That's the essence of Maat."

31. "In accepting this Gift you will unlock wisdom and powers that were mapped out for you in the Duat. That's the secret that many people fail to understand. Being in harmony with your Destiny, unleashes the potential within you. It was written, so shall it be lived," Hetankhu emphasised.

32. Senebty interrupted again, "The way you put it, makes it sound easy. But it's not an easy thing to just uproot your life and follow another path. I understand all that you say. But I am still nervous about what is to come. What about the Dark Spirits, won't they attack me if I start practising and using this Gift?"

33. Hetankhu continued, "That's a good question. When you start using the Gift, there will be those

forces that will want to stop you from helping people, here on earth and in the Duat. But you have nothing to fear, for I will give you Hekau and teach you how to defend yourself and also attack if need be. The Ancestors will also protect your from the Duat. You have powerful Ancestors behind you, rest assured."

34. "So you are in very good hands, Senebty. You have nothing to worry about. The Ancestor that wants to use you is a very powerful and wise Priestess, as I said. Your bloodline is very special. I am actually glad that she wants to reveal herself and her powers again in the world. I had thought she wasn't going to come through, anytime soon, because she is very strict, particular and exacting like the Great Sage, the Sheps Imhotep." Senebty was put at ease by these last words.

35. Hetankhu smiled at the mention of Imhotep and continued, "You are the One. You have been chosen, my dear. And this, you must accept. Let the Light shine through. I will teach you and you shall be taken care of."

36. "How long will the whole process of Initiation take?" Asked Senebty.

37. "It is a lifetime journey. But the purification and graduation will take 14 months to put the pieces together. It is the Re-membering stage, that's what we call it. It is akin to Re-membering Ausar," she said.

38. Then just like that, with no warning, Hetankhu stood up as if to dismiss her and declared, "We start next week!"

39. "What? But... If only..." Senebty retorted.

40. That is how Senebty began the lifelong journey to become one of the Greatest Priestesses of Kamit that ever lived.

41. She became very skilful and proficient in all the crafts of spirituality, including astrology and herbology. She even went on to surpass her wise teacher. She could predict the future with ease, but she too used it sparingly. In this regard, she only counselled special and very important people, such as Kings and Queens, who were High Initiates. As Hetankhu had promised, the Ancestors brought her a man that she loved and had many healthy children with until she went to the Duat herself and became an Ancestor.

42. As it was written in the Duat, it was lived on Earth.

Chapter 8

PAUT SHEPSU

1. On the eleventh month of the year, Neferowa decided to do something special for her Shepsu Shrine, for the first eleven days of the month.

2. Like every other day, she washed herself in the morning and performed her morning rituals, so as to purify herself after waking up from dreaming in the Duat.

3. When approaching the shrine she proclaimed, "Ikheru Enen," and then bowed down in reverence. This was an act of prostration.

4. In Ancient Kamit, as well as all other African cultures, prostration before the Divine was always observed.

5. Conventionally, she would bow down when first addressing the Neteru and Shepsu shrines, and also when leaving their presence.

6. Neferowa prostrated by placing her hands up by the side of her head while on her knees and then bowing, and placing the forehead on the ground. As she came up she said, "Anetch Hrak!"

7. In her mind, due to the African wisdom and teaching that she had received from her parents and grandparents, she was bowing to the

Ancestor's wisdom. She knelt because they out-ranked her, and she was bowing to the Neter within the Shepsu.

8. She knew that it was the correct attitude and spirit to approaching the shrines, and also the Oracles. She came seeking something from the shrines, and so she was open and willing to surrender to them.

9. She approached the shrines to give offerings, as well as herself. She was giving her attention and energy. In this regard, she humbled herself.

10. Neferowa then lit the eleven white candles on the shrine. She also lit the frankincense and myrrh incense, placed a fresh cup of spring water and food on the shrine, exactly in that order.

11. She made sure that for today, and the subsequent ten days, she would pick the freshest fruits that she could find and prepare the best meals possible.

12. While facing the shrine, she then poured libations, starting first with Neter and the Neteru.

13. She followed with the Paut Shepsu and professed, "Salutation of Power Father-Mother Creator Being, who comes as the Exalted Ancestors, thank you for the wisdom, thank you for the power, and thank you for life!"

14. She then continued to praise the rest of the Paut Shepsu that she could remember from Ancient Kamit. This was a Living and Breathing List that she updated from time to time, whenever her spiritual teacher told her to add on to the list.

15. She said the following words with vigour and passion:

16. Praise be to thee O Sheps Ausar SiKa. Anetch Hrak!

17. Praise be to thee O Sheps Ausar Kiyu. Anetch Hrak!

18. Praise be to thee O Sheps Ausar Tiyu. Anetch Hrak!
19. Praise be to thee O Sheps Ausar Thesh. Anetch Hrak!
20. Praise be to thee O Sheps Ausar Neheb. Anetch Hrak!
21. Praise be to thee O Sheps Ausar Wezner. Anetch Hrak!
22. Praise be to thee O Sheps Ausar Mekh. Anetch Hrak!
23. Praise be to thee O Sheps Ausar Zerq. Anetch Hrak!
24. Praise be to thee O Sheps Ausar Ka. Anetch Hrak!
25. Praise be to thee O Sheps Ausar Heru Ra. Anetch Hrak!
26. Praise be to thee O Sheps Ausar Narmer. Anetch Hrak!
27. Praise be to thee O Sheps Ausar Heru Aha. Anetch Hrak!
28. Praise be to thee O Sheps Ausar Jer. Anetch Hrak!
29. Praise be to thee O Sheps Ausar Jet. Anetch Hrak!
30. Praise be to thee O Sheps Ausar Den. Anetch Hrak!
31. Praise be to thee O Sheps Ausar Anejib. Anetch Hrak!
32. Praise be to thee O Sheps Ausar Semerkhet. Anetch Hrak!
33. Praise be to thee O Sheps Ausar Qua. Anetch Hrak!
34. Praise be to thee O Sheps Ausar Hetep Shekhemi. Anetch Hrak!
35. Praise be to thee O Sheps Ausar Neb Ra. Anetch Hrak!
36. Praise be to thee O Sheps Ausar Neter En. Anetch Hrak!
37. Praise be to thee O Sheps Ausar Wineg. Anetch Hrak!
38. Praise be to thee O Sheps Ausar Sened. Anetch Hrak!

39. Praise be to thee O Sheps Ausar Peribsen. Anetch Hrak!

40. Praise be to thee O Sheps Ausar Khashekhemi. Anetch Hrak!

41. Praise be to thee O Sheps Ausar Senkhet. Anetch Hrak!

42. Praise be to thee O Sheps Ausar Neterrakhet. Anetch Hrak!

43. Praise be to thee O Sheps Ausar Shekhemkhet. Anetch Hrak!

44. Praise be to thee O Sheps Ausar Khaba. Anetch Hrak!

45. Praise be to thee O Sheps Ausar Qua Hejet Huni. Anetch Hrak!

46. Praise be to thee O Sheps Ausar Khufu. Anetch Hrak!

47. Praise be to thee O Sheps Ausar Jedef-Ra. Anetch Hrak!

48. Praise be to thee O Sheps Ausar Khaf-Ra. Anetch Hrak!

49. Praise be to thee O Sheps Ausar Menkau-Ra. Anetch Hrak!

50. Praise be to thee O Sheps Ausar Sheps Ka-ef. Anetch Hrak!

51. Praise be to thee O Sheps Ausar Userer Ka Ra. Anetch Hrak!

52. Praise be to thee O Sheps Ausar Sahu Ra. Anetch Hrak!

53. Praise be to thee O Sheps Ausar Neferer Ka Ra. Anetch Hrak!

54. Praise be to thee O Sheps Ausar Sheps s Ka Ra. Anetch Hrak!

55. Praise be to thee O Sheps Ausar Neferef Ra. Anetch Hrak!

56. Praise be to thee O Sheps Ausar Niuser Ra. Anetch Hrak!

57. Praise be to thee O Sheps Ausar Men Kau Heru. Anetch Hrak!

58. Praise be to thee O Sheps Ausar Jed Ka Ra. Anetch Hrak!

59. Praise be to thee O Sheps Ausar Unas. Anetch Hrak!

60. Praise be to thee O Sheps Ausar Teti. Anetch Hrak!

61. Praise be to thee O Sheps Ausar User Ka Ra. Anetch Hrak!

62. Praise be to thee O Sheps Ausar Pepi. Anetch Hrak!

63. Praise be to thee O Sheps Ausar Meri en Ra. Anetch Hrak!

64. Praise be to thee O Sheps Ausar Nefer Ka Ra Pepi. Anetch Hrak!

65. Praise be to thee O Sheps Ausar Neter Ka Sepit. Anetch Hrak!

66. Praise be to thee O Sheps Ausar Neter Ka Ra. Anetch Hrak!

67. Praise be to thee O Sheps Ausar Men Ka Ra. Anetch Hrak!

68. Praise be to thee O Sheps Ausar Nefer Ka Ra. Anetch Hrak!

69. Praise be to thee O Sheps Ausar Jed Ka Ra. Anetch Hrak!

70. Praise be to thee O Sheps Ausar Nefer Ka Ra. Anetch Hrak!

71. Praise be to thee O Sheps Ausar Snefer Ka. Anetch Hrak!

72. Praise be to thee O Sheps Ausar Ni Ka Ra. Anetch Hrak!

73. Praise be to thee O Sheps Ausar Turtu. Anetch Hrak!

74. Praise be to thee O Sheps Ausar Nefer Ka Heru. Anetch Hrak!

75. Praise be to thee O Sheps Ausar Pepi Seneb. Anetch Hrak!
76. Praise be to thee O Sheps Ausar Nefer Ka Men. Anetch Hrak!
77. Praise be to thee O Sheps Ausar Iby. Anetch Hrak!
78. Praise be to thee O Sheps Ausar Nefer Kau Ra. Anetch Hrak!
79. Praise be to thee O Sheps Ausar Nefer Kau Heru. Anetch Hrak!
80. Praise be to thee O Sheps Ausar Neferer Ka Ra. Anetch Hrak!
81. Praise be to thee O Sheps Ausar Uj Ka Ra. Anetch Hrak!
82. Praise be to thee O Sheps Ausar Shekhem Ka Ra. Anetch Hrak!
83. Praise be to thee O Sheps Ausar Ity. Anetch Hrak!
84. Praise be to thee O Sheps Ausar Imhetep. Anetch Hrak!
85. Praise be to thee O Sheps Ausar Isu. Anetch Hrak!
86. Praise be to thee O Sheps Ausar Yitenu. Anetch Hrak!
87. Praise be to thee O Sheps Ausar Kheti. Anetch Hrak!
88. Praise be to thee O Sheps Ausar Neb Kau Ra Kheti. Anetch Hrak!
89. Praise be to thee O Sheps Ausar Nefer Ka Ra. Anetch Hrak!
90. Praise be to thee O Sheps Ausar Meri Ka Ra. Anetch Hrak!
91. Praise be to thee O Sheps Ausar Ity. Anetch Hrak!
92. Praise be to thee O Sheps Ausar Muntu Hotep. Anetch Hrak!
93. Praise be to thee O Sheps Ausar Intef. Anetch Hrak!
94. Praise be to thee O Sheps Ausar Amen M Hot. Anetch Hrak!

95. Praise be to thee O Sheps Ausar Useretzen. Anetch Hrak!

96. Praise be to thee O Sheps Ausar Amen em Hot. Anetch Hrak!

97. Praise be to thee O Sheps Ausar Sebek Neferu. Anetch Hrak!

98. Praise be to thee O Sheps Ausar Sebek Hetep. Anetch Hrak!

99. Praise be to thee O Sheps Ausar Shekhem Ka Ra. Anetch Hrak!

100. Praise be to thee O Sheps Ausar Hetep Ra. Anetch Hrak!

101. Praise be to thee O Sheps Ausar Sebek en Sif. Anetch Hrak!

102. Praise be to thee O Sheps Ausar Shekhem Uj Tui Ra. Anetch Hrak!

103. Praise be to thee O Sheps Ausar Intef. Anetch Hrak!

104. Praise be to thee O Sheps Ausar Yahmesh. Anetch Hrak!

105. Praise be to thee O Sheps Ausar Shekhem Sa Kho Ra. Anetch Hrak!

106. Praise be to thee O Sheps Ausar Sebek em Sa ef. Anetch Hrak!

107. Praise be to thee O Sheps Ausar Ta Owa. Anetch Hrak!

108. Praise be to thee O Sheps Ausar Ka Mesh. Anetch Hrak!

109. Praise be to thee O Sheps Ausar Yah Mesh. Anetch Hrak!

110. Praise be to thee O Sheps Ausar Amen Hotep. Anetch Hrak!

111. Praise be to thee O Sheps Ausar Tehuti Mesh. Anetch Hrak!

112. Praise be to thee O Sheps Ausar Amen em Hot Shepsut. Anetch Hrak!

113. Praise be to thee O Sheps Ausar Tehuti Mesh. Anetch Hrak!

114. Praise be to thee O Sheps Ausar Amen Hotep. Anetch Hrak!

115. Praise be to thee O Sheps Ausar Tehuti Mesh. Anetch Hrak!

116. Praise be to thee O Sheps Ausar Amen Hotep. Anetch Hrak!

117. Praise be to thee O Sheps Ausar Heru M Heb. Anetch Hrak!

118. Praise be to thee O Sheps Ausar Ra Meshu. Anetch Hrak!

119. Praise be to thee O Sheps Ausar Meri N Ptah Seti. Anetch Hrak!

120. Praise be to thee O Sheps Ausar User-Maat-Ra Setep-en-Ra Ra-Meshu-Meri-Amen. Anetch Hrak!

121. Praise be to thee O Sheps Ausar Meri en Ptah. Anetch Hrak!

122. Praise be to thee O Sheps Ausar Amen em Mesh. Anetch Hrak!

123. Praise be to thee O Sheps Ausar Meri en Ptah Seti. Anetch Hrak!

124. Praise be to thee O Sheps Ausar Si Ptah. Anetch Hrak!

125. Praise be to thee O Sheps Ausar Ta Useretsen. Anetch Hrak!

126. Praise be to thee O Sheps Ausar Set en Khet. Anetch Hrak!

127. Praise be to thee O Sheps Ausar Ra Meshzez. Anetch Hrak!

128. Praise be to thee O Sheps Ausar Piye. Anetch Hrak!

129. Praise be to thee O Sheps Ausar Shabaka. Anetch Hrak!

130. Praise be to thee O Sheps Ausar Shabitka. Anetch Hrak!

131. Praise be to thee O Sheps Ausar Taharka. Anetch Hrak!

132. Praise be to thee O Sheps Ausar Tenutemni. Anetch Hrak!

133. Praise be to thee O Sheps Ausar Hordedef. Anetch Hrak!

134. Praise be to thee O Sheps Ausar Ka Khepera Seneb. Anetch Hrak!

135. Praise be to thee O Sheps Ausar Ptah Hotep. Anetch Hrak!

136. Praise be to thee O Sheps Ausar Ptah em Tehuti. Anetch Hrak!

137. Praise be to thee O Sheps Ausar Imhotep. Anetch Hrak!

138. Praise be to thee O Sheps Ausar Khety. Anetch Hrak!

139. Praise be to thee O Sheps Ausar Neferti. Anetch Hrak!

140. Praise be to thee O Sheps Ausar Ka ir es. Anetch Hrak!

141. After she finished with the Paut Shepsu list, she then praised and thanked her own personal list of Ancestors.

142. Neferowa finished the libations by saying, "Tua Neter, Tua Neter, Tua Neter! Anetch Hrak!"

143. After having saluted the rank and file of her entire being and life, she then continued onwards with her daily chores, feeling revitalised and ready for action.

144. She was grateful for her African Wisdom, History, Culture, Tradition and Spirituality. She knew that without it she would have no foundation, no roots and no vision to stand on. She would be like a tree with no roots. She always remembered what Neter affirmed in the creation of the world, "I found no place whereon I could stand. I laid a foundation of all things by Maat."

145. This is what African Spirituality (**AS**) was about to her. It was the same foundation that Neter used to build the world. It was Maat.

146. In Maat she had found something that she could stand on, whenever the world and people were unkind to her.

147. Maat was her foundation as well.

148. "If Maat was good enough for Neter to build the world on, it was good enough for her too," she used to declare to herself every day, repeatedly.

149. She appreciated and respected her upbringing from her African parents, because they had instilled in her that sense of pride and belonging to her community, society and people.

150. This is what drove her to succeed and be a positive contributing member of her community, because she knew that she belonged.

151. Africa was her home. Maat was her foundation. The Ancestors were her guide. Neter and the Neteru were her spiritual and physical makeup.

152. "Tua Neter! Tua Neteru! Tua Shepsu!"

BOOK OF AFRICAN SPIRITUALITY

Book of Geb

Chapter 1

BOOK OF PTAH HOTEP

A. The Instruction of the Governor of his city, the Vizier, Ptah-Hotep, in the Reign of the King of Upper and Lower Kamit, Isosi, living forever, to the end of Time.

B. The Governor of his city, the Vizier, Ptah-Hotep, he said: "O Prince my Lord, the end of life is at hand, old age descends, upon me, feebleness cometh, and childishness is renewed. He that is old lies down in misery every day. The eyes are small, the ears are deaf. Energy is diminished, the heart has no rest. The mouth is silent, and he speaks no word, the heart stops, and he remembers not yesterday. The bones are painful throughout the body, good turns into evil. All taste departs. These things doeth old age for mankind, being evil in all things. The nose is stopped, and he breathes not for weakness, whether standing or sitting.

C. "Command thy servant, therefore, to make over my, princely authority, to my son. Let me speak unto him the words of them that hearken to the counsel of the men of old time, those that once hearkened unto the Neteru. I pray thee, let this thing be done, that Isfet may be banished from among persons of understanding, that thou may enlighten the lands."

D. Said the Majesty of this Neter: "Instruct him, then, in the words of old time, may he be a wonder unto the children of princes, that they may enter and hearken with him. Make straight all their hearts, and discourse with him, without causing weariness."

E. Here begin the proverbs of fair speech, spoken by the Hereditary Chief, the Father, Beloved of the Neter, the Eldest Son of the King, of his body, the Governor of his city, the Vizier, Ptah-Hotep, when instructing the ignorant in the knowledge of exactness in fair speaking, the glory of him that obeys, the shame of him that transgresses them. He said unto his son:

1. Be not proud because thou art learned, but discourse with the ignorant man, as with the sage. For no limit can be set to skill, neither is there any craftsman that possesses full advantages. Fair speech is rarer than the emerald that is found by maidens on the pebbles.

2. If thou find an arguer talking, one that is well disposed and wiser than thou, let thine arms fall, bend thy back, be not angry with him if he agrees not with thee. Refrain from speaking evil, oppose him not at any time when he speaks. If he addresses thee as one ignorant of the matter, thine humbleness shall bear away his contentions.

3. If thou find an arguer talking, thy fellow, one that is within thy reach, keep not silence when he says anything that is evil, so shalt thou be wiser than he. Great will be the applause on the part of the listeners, and thy name shall be good in the knowledge of princes.

4. If thou find an arguer talking, a poor man, that is to say not thine equal, be not scornful toward

him because he is lowly. Let him alone, then shall he confound himself. Question him not to please thine heart, neither pour out thy wrath upon him that is before thee, it is shameful to confuse a mean mind. If thou be about to do that which is in thine heart, overcome it as a thing rejected of princes.

5. If thou be a leader, as one directing the conduct of the multitude, endeavour always to be gracious, that thine own conduct be without defect. Great is Truth, appointing a straight path, never has it been overthrown since the reign of Ausar. One that oversteps the laws shall be punished. Overstepping is by the covetous man, but degradations bear off his riches. Never has evildoing, brought its venture safe to port. For he says, "I will obtain by myself for myself," and says not, "I will obtain because I am allowed." But the limits of justice are steadfast, it is that which a man repeats from his father.

6. Cause not fear among men, for this, the Neter punishes likewise. For there is a man that says, "Therein is life," and he is bereft of the bread of his mouth. There is a man that says, "Power is therein," and he says, "I seize for myself that which I perceive." Thus a man speaks, and he is smitten down. It is another that attains by giving unto him that has not. Never has that which men have prepared for come to pass, for what the Neter has commanded, even that thing comes to pass. Live, therefore, in the house of kindliness, and men shall come and give gifts of themselves.

7. If thou be among the guests of a man that is greater than thou, accept that which he gives thee, putting it to thy lips. If thou look at him that is

before thee, thine host, pierce him not with many glances. It is abhorred of the soul to stare at him. Speak not until he addresses thee, one knows not what may be evil in his opinion. Speak when he questions thee, so shall thy speech be good in his opinion. The noble who sits before the food is divided, as his soul moves him, he gives unto him that he would favour. It is the custom of the evening meal. It is his soul that guides his hand. It is the noble that bestows, not the underling that attains. Thus the eating of bread is under the providence of the Neter, he is an ignorant man that disputes it.

8.   If thou be an emissary sent from one noble to another, be exact after the manner of him that sent thee, give his message even as he has said it. Beware of making enmity by thy words, setting one noble against the other by perverting truth. Overstep it not, neither repeat that which any man, be he prince or peasant, says in opening the heart, it is abhorrent to the soul.

9.   If thou have ploughed, gather thine harvest in the field, and the Neter shall make it great under thine hand. Fill not thy mouth at any neighbour's table. If a crafty man be the possessor of wealth, he steals like a crocodile from the priests. Let not a man be envious that has no children, let him be neither downcast nor quarrelsome on account of it. For a father, though great, may be grieved, as to the mother of children, she has less peace than another. Verily, each man is created, to his destiny, by the Neter, who is the chief of a tribe, trustful in following him.

10.	If thou be lowly, serve a wise man, that all thine actions may be good before the Neter. If thou have known a man of none account that has been advanced in rank, be not haughty toward him on account of that which thou knows concerning him, but honour him that has been advanced, according to that which he has become. Behold, riches come not of themselves, it is their rule for him that desires them. If he bestirs him and collects them himself, the Neter shall make him prosperous, but he shall punish him, if he be slothful.

11.	Follow thine heart during thy lifetime, do not more than is commanded thee. Diminish not the time of following the heart. It is abhorred of the soul, that its time of ease be taken away. Shorten not the daytime more than is needful to maintain thy house. When riches are gained, follow the heart, for riches are of no avail if one be weary.

12.	If thou would be a wise man, beget a son for the pleasing of the Neter. If he make straight his course after thine example, if he arrange thine affairs in due order, do unto him all that is good, for thy son is he, begotten of thine own soul. Sunder not thine heart from him, or thine own begotten shall curse thee. If he be heedless and trespass thy rules of conduct, and is violent, if every speech that comes from his mouth be a vile word, then beat thou him, that his talk may be fitting. Keep him from those that make light of that which is commanded, for it is they that make him rebellious. And they that are guided go not astray, but they that lose their bearings cannot find a straight course.

13. If thou be in the chamber of council, act always according to the steps enjoined on thee at the beginning of the day. Be not absent, or thou shalt be expelled, but be ready in entering and making report. Wide is the seat of one that has made address. The council chamber acts by strict rule, and all its plans are in accordance with method. It is the Neter that advances one to a seat therein, the like is not done for elbowers.

14. If thou be among people, make for thyself love, the beginning and end of the heart. One that knows not his course shall say in himself seeing thee, "He that orders himself duly becomes the owner of wealth, I shall copy his conduct." Thy name shall be good, though thou speak not, thy body shall be fed, thy face shall be seen among thy neighbours, thou shall be provided with what thou lacks. As to the man whose heart obeys his belly, he causes disgust in place of love. His heart is wretched, his body is gross, he is insolent toward those endowed of the Neter. He that obeys his belly has an enemy.

15. Report thine actions without concealment. Discover thy conduct when in council with thine overlord. It is not evil for the envoy that his report be not answered. "Yea, I know it," by the prince, for that which he knows includes not this. If he, the prince, thinks that he will oppose him on account of it, he thinks, "He will be silent because I have spoken."

16. If thou be a leader, cause that the rules that thou hast enjoined be carried out, and do all things as one that remembers the days coming after, when

speech avails not. Be not lavish of favours, it leads to servility, producing slackness.

17. If thou be a leader, be gracious when thou hearkens unto the speech of a suppliant. Let him not hesitate to deliver himself of that which he has thought to tell thee, but be desirous of removing his injury. Let him speak freely, that the thing for which he has come to thee may be done. If he hesitates to open his heart, it is said, "Is it because he, the judge, does the wrong that no entreaties are made to him concerning it by those to whom it happens?" But a well taught heart hearkens readily.

18. If thou desire to continue friendship in any abode wherein thou interest, be it as master, as brother, or as friend, wheresoever thou goes, beware of consorting with women. No place prospers wherein that is done. Nor is it prudent to take part in it, a thousand men have been ruined for the pleasure of a little time, short as a dream. Even death is reached thereby, it is a wretched thing. As for the evil doer, one leaves him for what he does, he is avoided. If his desires be not gratified, he regards no laws.

19. If thou desire that thine actions may be good, save thyself from all malice, and beware of the quality of covetousness, which is a grievous inner malady. Let it not chance that thou fall thereinto. It sets at variance fathers-in-law and the kinsmen of the daughter-in-law. It separates the wife and the husband. It gathers unto itself all evils. It is the girdle of all wickedness. But the man that is just flourishes, truth goes in his footsteps, and he

makes habitations therein, not in the dwelling of covetousness.

20. Be not covetous, in seizing that which is not thine own property. Be not covetous toward thy neighbours, for with a gentleman praise avails more than might. He, that is covetous, comes empty from among his neighbours, being void of the persuasion of speech. One has remorse for even a little covetousness when his belly cools.

21. If thou would be wise, provide for thine house, and love thy wife that is in thine arms. Fill her stomach, clothe her back, oil is the remedy for her limbs. Gladden her heart during thy lifetime, for she is an estate profitable unto its lord. Be not harsh, for gentleness masters her more than strength. Give to her that for which she sighs and that toward which her eye looks, so shall thou keep her in thy house.

22. Satisfy thine hired servants out of such things as thou has. It is the duty of one that has been favoured by the Neter. In truth, it is hard to satisfy hired servants. For one says, "He is a lavish person, one knows not that which may come, from him." But on the morrow he thinks, "He is a person of exactitude, parsimony, content therein." And when favours have been shown unto servants, they say, "We go." Peace dwells not in that town, wherein dwells servants that are wretched.

23. Repeat not extravagant speech, neither listen thereto, for it is the utterance of a body heated by wrath. When such speech is repeated to thee, hearken not thereto, look to the ground. Speak not regarding it, that he that is before thee, may know wisdom. If thou be commanded to do a

theft, bring it to pass that the command be taken off thee, for it is a thing hateful according to law. That which destroys a vision is the veil over it.

24. If thou would be a wise man, and one sitting in council with his overlord, apply thine heart unto perfection. Silence is more profitable unto thee than abundance of speech. Consider how thou may be opposed by an expert that speaks in council. It is a foolish thing to speak on every kind of work, for he that disputes thy words shall put them unto proof.

25. If thou be powerful, make thyself to be honoured for knowledge and for gentleness. Speak with authority, that is, not as if following injunctions, for he that is humble, when highly placed, falls into errors. Exalt not thine heart, that it be not brought low. Be not silent, but beware of interruption and of answering words with heat. Put it far from thee, control thyself. The wrathful heart speaks fiery words. It darts out at the man of peace that approaches, thereby stopping his path. One that reckons accounts all-day passes not a happy moment. One that gladdens his heart all-day provides not for his house. The bowman hits the mark, as the steersman reaches land, by diversity of aim. He that obeys his heart shall command.

26. Let not a prince be hindered when he is occupied, neither oppress, the heart of him that is already laden, for he shall be hostile toward one that delays him, but shall bare his soul unto one that loves him. The disposal of souls is with the Neter, and that which he loves is his creation. Set out, therefore, after a violent quarrel, be at peace with

him that is hostile unto his opponent. It is such souls that make love to grow.

27. Instruct a noble in such things as be profitable unto him, cause that he be received among men. Let his satisfaction fall on his master, for thy provision depends upon his will. By reason of it thy belly shall be satisfied, thy back will be clothed thereby. Let him receive thine heart, that thine house may flourish and thine honour, if thou wish it to flourish, thereby. He shall extend thee a kindly hand. Further, he shall implant the love of thee in the bodies of thy friends. Forsooth, it is a soul loving to hearken.

28. If thou be the son of a man of the priesthood, and an envoy to conciliate the multitude, speak thou without favouring one side. Let it not be said: "His conduct is that of the nobles, favouring one side in his speech." Turn thine aim toward exact judgments.

29. If thou have been gracious at a former time, having forgiven a man to guide him aright, shun him, remind him not after the first day that he has been silent to thee, concerning it.

30. If thou be great, after being of none account, and has gotten riches after squalor, being foremost in these in the city, and has knowledge concerning useful matters, so that promotion is come unto thee, then swathe not thine heart in thine hoard, for thou art become the steward of the endowments of the Neter. Thou art not the last, another shall be thine equal, and to him shall come fortune and the station.

31. Bend thy back unto thy chief, thine overseer in the King's palace, for thine house depends upon

his wealth and thy wages in their season. How foolish is one that quarrels with his chief, for one lives only while he is gracious?

32. Plunder not the houses of tenants. Neither steal the things of a friend, lest he accuse thee in thine bearing, which thrusts back the heart. If he know of it, he will do thee an injury. Quarrelling in place of friendship is a foolish thing.

33. If thou would seek out the nature of a friend, ask it not of any companion of his, but pass a time with him alone, that thou injure not his affairs. Debate with him after a season. Test his heart in an occasion of speech. When he has told thee his past life, he has made an opportunity that thou may either be ashamed for him or be familiar with him. Be not reserved with him when he opens speech, neither answer him after a scornful manner. Withdraw not thyself from him, neither interrupt him whose matter is not yet ended, whom it is possible to benefit.

34. Let thy face be bright for the time thou lives. That which goes into the storehouse must come out therefrom, and bread is to be shared. He that is grasping in entertainment shall himself have an empty belly, he that causes strife, comes himself to sorrow. Take not such a person for thy companion. It is a man's kindly acts that are remembered of him in the years after his life.

35. Know well thy merchants, for when thine affairs are in evil case, thy good repute among thy friends is a channel which is filled. It is more important than the dignities of a man, and the wealth of one passes to another. The good repute of a man's son

is a glory unto him, and a good character is for remembrance.

36. Correct chiefly, instruct conformably, therewith. Vice must be drawn out that virtue may remain. Nor is this a matter of misfortune, for one that is a gainsayer becomes a strifemaker.

37. If thou make a woman to be ashamed, wanton of heart, not known by her townsfolk, to be falsely placed, be kind unto her for a space, send her not away, give her food to eat. The wantonness of her heart shall esteem thy guidance. If thou obey these things that I have said unto thee, thy entire demeanour shall be of the best, for verily, the quality of truth is among their excellences. Set the memory of them in the mouths of the people, for their proverbs are good. Nor shall any word that has been set down here cease out of this land for ever, but shall be made a pattern whereby princes shall speak well. They, my words, shall instruct a man how he shall speak, after he has heard them, certainly, he shall become as one skilful in obeying, excellent in speaking, after he has heard them. Good fortune shall befall him, for he shall be of the highest rank. He shall be gracious to the end of his life, he shall be contented always. His knowledge shall be his guide into a place of security, wherein he shall prosper while on earth. The scholar shall be content in his knowledge. As to the prince, in his turn, in truth, his heart shall be happy, his tongue made straight. And in these proverbs, his lips shall speak, his eyes shall see, and his ears shall hear that which is profitable for his son, so that he deals justly, whilst void of deceit.

38. A splendid thing is the obedience of an obedient son. He comes in and listens obediently. Excellent in hearing, excellent in speaking, is every man that obeys what is noble, and the obedience of an obeyer is a noble thing. Obedience is better than all things that are, it makes goodwill. How good it is that a son should take that from his father by which he has reached old age, obedience. That which is desired by the Neter is obedience. Disobedience is abhorred by the Neter. Verily, it is the heart that makes its master to obey or to disobey, for the safe and sound life of a man is his heart. It is the obedient man that obeys what is said, he that loves to obey, the same shall carry out commands. He that obeys becomes one obeyed. It is good indeed when a son obeys his father, and he, his father, that has spoken has great joy of it. Such a son shall be mild as a master, and he that hears him shall obey him that has spoken. He shall be comely in body and honoured by his father. His memory shall be in the mouths of the living, those upon earth, as long as they exist.

39. Let a son receive the word of his father, not being heedless of any rule of his. Instruct thy son thus, for the obedient man is one that is perfect in the opinion of princes. If he direct his mouth by what has been enjoined him, watchful and obedient, thy son shall be wise, and his going seemly. Heedlessness leads into disobedience on the morrow, but understanding shall establish him. As for the fool, he shall be crushed.

40. As for the fool, devoid of obedience, he does nothing. Knowledge, he regards as ignorance. Profitable things are hurtful things and he does

all kinds of errors, so that he is rebuked therefore every day. He lives in death therewith, it is his food. At chattering speech he marvels, as at the wisdom of princes, living in death every day. He is shunned because of his misfortunes, by reason of the multitude of afflictions that come upon him every day.

41. A son that hearkens is as a follower of Heru. He is good after he hearkens, he grows old, he reaches honour and reverence. He repeats in like manner to his sons and daughters, so renewing the instruction of his father. Each man instructs as did his begetter, repeating it unto his children. Let them, in turn, speak with their sons and daughters, that they may be famous in their deeds. Let that which thou speak implant true things and just in the life of thy children. Then the highest authority shall arrive, and chaos departs from them. And such men that see these things shall say, "Surely that man has spoken to good purpose," and they shall do likewise, or, "But surely that man was experienced." And all people shall declare, "It is they that shall direct the multitude, dignities are not complete without them." Take not my word away, neither add one, set not one in the place of another. Be wary of speech when a learned man hearkens unto thee. Desire to be established for good in the mouth of those that hear thee speaking. If thou have entered as an expert, speak with exact lips, that thy conduct may be seemly.

42. Be thine heart overflowing, but refrain thy mouth. Let thy conduct be exact while amongst nobles, and seemly before thy lord, doing that which he has commanded. Such a son shall speak unto

them that hearken to him. Moreover, his begetter shall be favoured. Apply thine heart, what time thou speaks to saying things such that the nobles who listen declare, "How excellent is that which comes out of his mouth!"

43. Carry out the behest of thy lord to thee. How good is the teaching of a man's father, for he has come from him, who has spoken of his son while he was yet unborn, that which is done for him, the son, is more than that which is commanded him. In truth, a good son is a gift from Neter, he does more than is enjoined on him. He does right, and puts his heart into his entire goings. If now thou attain thy position, the body shall flourish, the King shall be content in all that thou does, and thou shalt gather years of life not fewer than I have passed upon earth. I have gathered even more years of life, for the King has bestowed upon me favours more than upon my forefathers, this because I wrought truth and justice for the King unto mine old age.

Chapter 2

BOOK OF KAGEMNI

1. The cautious man flourishes, the exact one is praised, the innermost chamber opens unto the man of silence. Wide is the seat of the man gentle of speech, but knives are prepared against one that forces a path, that he advances not, save in due season.

2. If thou sit with a company of people, desire not the bread that thou likes, short is the time of restraining the heart, and gluttony is an abomination, therein is the quality of a beast. A handful of water quenches the thirst, and a mouthful of melon supports the heart. A good thing stands for goodness, but some small thing stands for plenty. A base man is he that is governed by his belly, he departs only when he is no longer able to fill full his belly in men's houses.

3. If thou sit with a glutton, eat with him, then depart. If thou drink with a drunkard, accept his drink and his heart shall be satisfied. Refuse not meat when with a greedy man. Take that which he gives thee, set it not on one side, thinking that it will be a courteous thing.

4. If a man be lacking in good fellowship, no speech has any influence over him. He is sour of face toward the glad-hearted that are kindly to him, he is a grief unto his mother and his friends, and all men cry, "Let thy name be known, thou art silent in thy mouth when thou art addressed!"

5. Be not haughty because of thy might in the midst of thy young soldiers. Beware of making strife, for one knows not the things that the Neter will do when He punishes.

6. The Vizier caused his sons and daughters to be summoned, when he had finished the rules of the conduct of men. And they marvelled when they came to him. Then he said unto them, "Hearken unto everything that is in writing in this book, even as I have said it in adding unto profitable sayings." And they cast themselves on their bellies, and they read it, even as it was in writing. And it was better in their opinion than anything in this land unto its limits.

7. Now they were living when His Majesty, the King of upper and lower Kamit, Heuni, departed, and His Majesty, the King of upper and lower Kamit, Seneferu, was enthroned as a gracious king over the whole of this land. Then was Kagemni made Governor of his city and Vizier.

Chapter 3

BOOK OF AMENEMHET

Here begins the Instruction made by the Majesty of the King of upper and lower Kamit, Sehotepeb-Ra, son of the Sun, Amenemhet, the Justified. He speaks thus in discovering words of truth unto his son, the Lord of the World:

1. Shine forth, he says, even as the Neter. Hearken to that which I say unto thee, that thou may reign over the land, that thou may govern the world, that thou may excel in goodness.

2. Let one withdraw himself from his subordinates entirely. It befalls that mankind give their hearts unto one that causes them fear. Mix not among them alone, fill not thine heart with a brother, know not a trusted friend, make for thyself no familiar dependents, in these things is no satisfaction.

3. When thou lies down, have a care for thy very life, since friends exist not for a man in the day of misfortunes. I gave to the beggar, and caused the orphan to live, I made him that had not to attain, even as he that had.

4. But it was the eater of my food that made insurrection against me, to whom I gave mine

hands, he created disturbance thereby, they that arrayed them in my fine linen regarded me as a shadow, and it was they that anointed themselves with my spices that entered my harem.

5. My images are among the living, and my achievements are among men. But I have made a heroic story that has not been heard, a great feat of arms that has not been seen. Surely one fights for a lassoed ox that forgets yesterday, and good fortune is of no avail unto one that cannot perceive it.

6. It was after the evening meal, and night was come. I took for myself an hour of ease. I lay down upon my bed, for I was weary. My heart began to wander. I slept. And lo! Weapons were brandished, and there was conference concerning me. I acted as the serpent of the desert.

7. I awoke to fight, I was alone. I found one struck down, it was the captain of the guard. Had I received quickly the arms from his hand, I had driven back the dastards by smiting around. But he was not a brave man on that night, nor could I fight alone, an occasion of prowess comes not to one surprised. Thus was I.

8. Behold, then, vile things came to pass, for I was without thee, the courtiers knew not that I had passed on to thee, my power. I sat not with thee on the throne. Let me then, make my plans. Because I awed them not I was not unmindful of them, but mine heart brings not to remembrance the slackness of servants.

9. Have women ever gathered together assailants? Are assassins reared within my palace? Was the opening done by cutting through the ground?

The underlings were deceived as to what they did. But misfortunes have not come in my train since my birth, nor has there existed the equal of me as a doer of bravery.

10. I forced my way up to Elephantine. I went down unto the coast-lakes. I have stood upon the boundaries of the land, and I have seen its centre. I have set the limits of might, by my might, in my deeds.

11. I raised corn, I loved the Nile. The Nile begged of me every valley. In my reign none hungered, none thirsted therein. They were content in that which I did, saying concerning me, "Every commandment is met."

12. I overcame lions, I carried off crocodiles. I cast the Asiatics under my feet, I carried off the Asiatics. I caused the Asiatics to flee, even as hounds.

13. I have made me a house, adorned with gold, its ceilings with lapis lazuli, and its walls having deep foundations. Its doors are of copper, their bolts are of bronze. It is made for everlasting. Eternity is in awe of it. I know every dimension thereof, O Lord of the World!

14. There are diverse devices in buildings. I know the pronouncements of men when inquiring into its beauties, but they know not that it was without thee. O my Son, Senwesert, life, safe and sound, be to thee, by thy feet do I walk. Thou art after mine own heart, by thine eyes do I see, born in an hour of delight, with spirits that rendered thee praise.

15. Behold! That which I have done at the beginning, let me set it in order for thee at the end. Let me be the landing-place of that which is in thine

heart. All men together set the White Crown on the Offspring of the Neter, fixing it unto its due place. I shall begin thy praises when in the Boat of Ra. Thy kingdom has been from primeval time, not by my doing, who have done valiant things. Raise up monuments, make beautiful thy tomb. I have fought against him whom thou knows, for I desire not that he should be beside thy Majesty. Life, safe and sound, be to thee.

Chapter 4

BOOK OF AMENEMOPE

A. The beginning of the instruction about life, the guide for well-being, all the principles of official procedure, the duties of the courtiers, to know how to refute the accusation of one who made it, and to send back a reply to the one who wrote, to set one straight on the paths of life, and make him prosper on earth, to let his heart settle down in its chapel, as one who steers him clear of evil, to save him from the talk of others, as one who is respected in the speech of men.

B. Written by the African superintendent of the land, experienced in his office, the offspring of a scribe of the Beloved Land, the Superintendent of produce, who fixes the grain measure, who sets the grain tax amount for his lord, who registers the islands which appear as new land over the cartouche of His Majesty, and sets up the land mark at the boundary of the arable land, who protects the king by his tax rolls, and makes the Register of the Black Nation.

C. The black scribe who places the divine offerings for all the Neteru, the donor of land grants to the people, the African superintendent of grain who administers the food offerings, who supplies the storerooms with grain, a truly silent man in Tjeni in the Ta-wer nome, one whose verdict is "acquitted" in Ipu, the owner of a pyramid tomb on the west of Senut, as well as the owner of a memorial chapel in Abydos, Amenemope, the son of Kanakht, whose verdict is "acquitted" in the Ta-wer nome.

D. For his African son, the youngest of his children, the least of his family, Initiate of the mysteries of Min-Kamutef, Libation pourer of Wennofre, who introduces Heru upon the throne of his father, his tippet in his august sanctuary, the seer of the Mother of Neter, the inspector of the black cattle of the terrace of Min, who protects Min in his sanctuary, Hor-em-Maa-Kheru is his true name, a child of an official of Ipu, the son of the sistrum player of Shu and Tefnut, the chief singer of Heru, the Lady Tawosret. He Says:

1. Give your years and hear what is said, give your mind over to their interpretation: It is profitable to put them in your heart, but woe to him that neglects them! Let them rest in the shrine of your insides that they may act as a lock in your heart. Now when there comes a storm of words, they will be a mooring post on your tongue.

2. If you spend a lifetime with these things in your heart, you will find it good fortune, you will discover my words to be a treasure house of life, and your body will flourish upon earth.

3. Beware of stealing from a miserable man and of raging against the cripple.

4. Do not stretch out your hand to touch an old man, nor snip at the words of an elder.

5. Don't let yourself be involved in a fraudulent business, nor desire the carrying out of it, do not get tired because of being interfered with, nor return an answer on your own.

6. The evildoer, throw him in the canal, and he will bring back its slime. The north wind comes down and ends his appointed hour, it is joined to the tempest, the thunder is high, the crocodiles are nasty, O hot-headed man, what are you like? He cries out, and his voice reaches heaven. O Moon, make his crime manifest! Row that we may ferry the evil man away, for we will not act according to his evil nature, lift him up, give him your hand, and leave him in the hands of Neter, fill his gut with your own food that he may be sated and ashamed.

7. Something else of value in the heart of Neter is to stop and think before speaking.

8. Do not get into a quarrel with the argumentative man, nor incite him with words, proceed cautiously before an opponent, and give way to an adversary, sleep on it before speaking, for a storm come forth like fire in hay is the hot-headed man in his appointed time.

9. May you be restrained before him, leave him to himself, and Neter will know how to answer him.

10. If you spend your life with these things in your heart, your children shall behold them.

11. The hot-headed man in the temple is like a tree grown indoors, only for a moment does it put forth roots. It reaches its end in the carpentry shop, it is floated away far from its place, or fire is its funeral pyre.

12. The truly temperate man sets himself apart, he is like a tree grown in a sunlit field, but it flourishes, it doubles its yield, it stands before its owner, its fruit is something sweet, its shade is pleasant, and it reaches its end as a statue.

13. Do not take by violence the shares of the temple, do not be grasping, and you will find overabundance.

14. Do not take away a temple servant in order to acquire the property of another man.

15. Do not say today is the same as tomorrow, or how will matters come to pass?

16. When tomorrow comes, today is past, the deep waters sink from the canal bank, crocodiles are uncovered, the hippopotamuses are on dry land, and the fishes gasping for air, the wolves are fat, the wild fowl in festival, and the nets are drained.

17. Every temperate man in the temple says, "Great is the benevolence of Ra."

18. Fill yourself with silence, you will find life, and your body shall flourish upon earth.

19. Do not displace the surveyor's marker on the boundaries of the arable land, nor alter the position of the measuring line, do not be greedy for a plot of land, nor overturn the boundaries of a widow.

20. As for the road in the field worn down by time, he who takes it violently for fields, if he traps by deceptive attestations, will be lassoed by the might of the moon.

21. To one who has done this on earth, pay attention, for he is a weak enemy, he is an enemy overturned inside himself, life is taken from his eye, his household is hostile to the community, his storerooms are toppled over, his property taken from his children, and to someone else his possessions given.

22. Take care not to topple over the boundary marks of the arable land, not fearing that you will be

brought to court, man propitiates Neter by the might of the Lord when he sets straight the boundaries of the arable land.

23. Desire, then, to make yourself prosper, and take care for Neb-er-Tcher, do not trample on the furrow of someone else, their good order will be profitable for you.

24. So plough the fields, and you will find whatever you need, and receive the bread from your own threshing floor: Better is the bushel which Neter gives you than five thousand deceitfully gotten, they do not spend a day in the storehouse or warehouse, they are no use for dough for beer, their stay in the granary is short-lived, when morning comes they will be swept away.

25. Better, then, is poverty in the hand of Neter than riches in the storehouse, better is bread when the mind is at ease than riches with anxiety.

26. Do not set your heart upon seeking riches, for there is no one who can ignore Destiny and Fortune.

27. Do not set your thoughts on external matters: For every man there is his appointed time.

28. Do not exert yourself to seek out excess and your wealth will prosper for you, if riches come to you by theft they will not spend the night with you, as soon as day breaks they will not be in your household, although their places can be seen, they are not there.

29. When the earth opens up its mouth, it levels him and swallows him up, and it drowns him in the deep, they have made for themselves a great hole which suites them.

30. They have sunk themselves in the tomb, or they have made themselves wings like geese, and they fly up to the sky.

31. Do not be pleased with yourself because of riches acquired through robbery, neither complain about poverty.

32. If an officer commands one who goes in front of him, his company leaves him, the boat of the covetous is abandoned in the mud, while the boat of the truly temperate man sails on. When he rises you shall offer to the Aten, saying, "Grant me prosperity and health." And he will give you your necessities for life, and you will be safe from fear.

33. Set your good deeds throughout the world that you may greet everyone, they make rejoicing for the Uraeus, and spit against the Apep.

34. Keep your tongue safe from words of detraction, and you will be the loved one of the people, then you will find your place within the temple and your offerings among the bread deliveries of your lord, you will be revered, when you are concealed in your grave, and be safe from the might of Neter.

35. Do not accuse a man, when the news of an escape is concealed. If you hear something good or bad, say it outside, where it is not heard, set a good report on your tongue, while the bad thing is covered up inside you.

36. Do not fraternize with the hot-tempered man, nor approach him to converse.

37. Safeguard your tongue from answering your superior, and take care not to speak against him.

38. Do not allow him to cast words only to entrap you, and be not too free in your reply, with a man of your own station discuss the reply, and take

care of speaking thoughtlessly, when a man's heart is upset, words travel faster than wind and rain.

39. He is ruined and created by his tongue, and yet he speaks slander, he makes an answer deserving of a beating, for its work is evil, he sails among all the world, but his cargo is false words, he acts the ferryman in knitting words: He goes forth and comes back arguing.

40. But whether he eats or whether he drinks inside, his accusation waits for him without. The day when his evil deed is brought to court is a disaster for his children.

41. Even Khnum will straightway come, even Khnum will straightway come, the creator of the ill-tempered man whom he moulds and fires, he is like a wolf cub in the farmyard, and he turns one eye to the other, squinting, for he sets families to argue.

42. He goes before all the wind like clouds, he darkens his colour in the sun, he crocks his tail like a baby crocodile, he curls himself up to inflict harm, his lips are sweet, but his tongue is bitter, and fire burns inside him.

43. Do not fly up to join that man not fearing you will be brought to account.

44. Do not address your intemperate friend in your unrighteousness, nor destroy your own mind, do not say to him, "May you be praised," not meaning it when there is fear within you.

45. Do not converse falsely with a man, for it is the abomination of Neter.

46. Do not separate your mind from your tongue, all your plans will succeed. You will be important

before others, while you will be secure in the hand of Neter.

47. Neter detests one who falsifies words, his great abomination is duplicity.

48. Do not covet the property of the dependent, nor hunger for his bread, the property of a dependent blocks the throat, it is vomit for the gullet.

49. If he has engendered it by false oaths, his heart slips back inside him.

50. It is through the disaffected that success is lost, bad and good elude.

51. If you are at a loss before your superior, and are confused in your speeches, your flattering is turned back with curses and your humble action by beatings. Whoever fills the mouth with too much bread swallows it and spits up, so he is emptied of his good.

52. To the examination of a dependant give thought while the sticks touch him, and while all his people are fettered with manacles: Who is to have the execution?

53. When you are too free before your superior, then you are in bad favour with your subordinates, so steer away from the poor man on the road, that you may see him but keep clear of his property.

54. Do not covet the property of an official, and do not fill your mouth with too much food extravagantly, if he sets you to manage his property, respect his, and yours will prosper.

55. Do not deal with the intemperate man, nor associate yourself to a disloyal party.

56. If you are sent to transport straw, respect its account, if a man is detected in a dishonest transaction, never again will he be employed.

57. Do not lead a man astray with reed pen or papyrus document: It is the abomination of Neter.

58. Do not witness a false statement, nor remove a man from the list by your order, do not enrol someone who has nothing, nor make your pen be false.

59. If you find a large debt against a poor man, make it into three parts, release two of them and let one remain: You will find it a path of life and you will pass the night in sound sleep, in the morning you will find it like good news.

60. Better it is to be praised as one loved by men than wealth in the storehouse, better is bread when the mind is at ease than riches with troubles.

61. Do not pay attention to a person, nor exert yourself to seek out his hand, if he says to you, "take a bribe," it is not an insignificant matter to heed him, do not avert your glance from him, nor bend down your head, nor turn aside your gaze.

62. Address him with your words and say to him greetings, when he stops, your chance will come, do not repel him at his first approach, another time he will be brought to judgment.

63. Do well, and you will attain influence.

64. Do not dip your reed against the one who sins.

65. The beak of the Ibis is the finger of the scribe, take care not to disturb it, the Ape rests in the temple of Khmun, while his eye travels around the Two Lands, if he sees one who sins with his finger, that is, a false scribe, he takes away his provisions by the flood.

66. As for a scribe who sins with his finger, his son shall not be enrolled.

67. If you spend your life with these things in your heart, your children shall see them.

68. Do not unbalance the scale nor make the weights false, nor diminish the fractions of the grain measure.

69. Do not wish for the grain measures of the fields and then cast aside those of the treasury.

70. The Ape sits by the balance, while his heart is the plummet. Where is a Neter as great as Tehuti, the one who discovered these things, to create them?

71. Do not get for yourself short weights, they are plentiful, indeed, an army by the might of Neter.

72. If you see someone cheating, at a distance you must pass him by.

73. Do not be avaricious for copper, and abjure fine clothes, what good is one cloaked in fine linen, when he cheats before Neter.

74. When gold is heaped upon gold, at daybreak it turns to lead.

75. Beware of robbing the grain measure to falsify its fractions, do not act wrongfully through force, although it is empty inside, may you have it measure exactly as to its size, your hand stretching out with precision.

76. Make not for yourself a measure of two capacities, for then it is toward the depths that you will go.

77. The measure is the eye of Ra. Its abomination is the one who takes.

78. As for a grain measurer who multiplies and subtracts, his eye will seal up against him.

79. Do not receive the harvest tax of a cultivator, nor bind up a papyrus against him to lead him astray.

80. Do not enter into collusion with the grain measurer, nor play with the seed allotment, more

important is the threshing floor for barley than swearing by the Great Throne.

81. Do not go to bed fearing tomorrow, for when day breaks what is tomorrow? Man knows not what tomorrow is!

82. Neter is success, man is failure.

83. The words which men say pass on one side, the things which Neter does pass on another side.

84. Do not say, "I am without fault," nor try to seek out trouble.

85. Fault is the business of Neter. It is locked up with his seal.

86. There is no success in the hand of Neter, nor is there failure before him, if he turns himself about to seek out success, in a moment he destroys him.

87. Be strong in your heart, make your mind firm, do not steer with your tongue, the tongue of a man is the steering oar of a boat, and Neb-er-Tcher is its pilot.

88. Do not enter the council chamber in the presence of a magistrate and then falsify your speech.

89. Do not go up and down with your accusation when your witnesses stand readied.

90. Do not overstate through oaths in the name of your lord, through pleas in the place of questioning.

91. Tell the truth before the magistrate, lest he gain power over your body, If you come before him the next day, he will concur with all you say, he will present your case in court before the Council of the Thirty, and it will be lenient another time as well.

92. Do not corrupt the people of the law court, nor put aside the just man, do not agree because of garments of white, nor accept one in rags.

93. Take not the gift of the strong man, nor repress the weak for him.

94. Justice is a wonderful gift of Neter, and he will render it to whomever he wishes.

95. The strength of one like him saves a poor wretch from his beatings.

96. Do not make false enrolment lists, for they are a serious affair deserving death, they are serious oaths of the kind promising not to misuse an office, and they are to be investigated by an informer.

97. Do not falsify the oracles on a papyrus and thereby alter the designs of Neter.

98. Do not arrogate to yourself the might of Neter as if Destiny and Fortune did not exist.

99. Hand property over to its rightful owners, and seek out life for yourself, let not your heart build in their house, for then your neck will be on the execution block.

100. Do not say, I have found a strong protector and now I can challenge a man in my town.

101. Do not say, I have found an active intercessor, and now I can challenge him whom I hate.

102. Indeed, you cannot know the plans of Neter, you cannot perceive tomorrow.

103. Sit yourself at the hands of Neter: Your tranquillity will cause them to open.

104. As for the crocodile deprived of his tongue, the fear of him is negligible.

105. Empty not your soul to everybody and do not diminish thereby your importance.

106. Do not circulate your words to others, nor fraternize with one who is too candid.

107. Better is a man whose knowledge is inside him than one who talks to disadvantage.

108. One cannot run to attain perfection, and one cannot create only to destroy it.

109. Do not castigate your companion in a dispute, and do not let him say his innermost thoughts.

110. Do not fly up to greet him when you do not see how he acts.

111. May you first comprehend his accusation and cool down your opponent.

112. Leave it to him and he will empty his soul, sleep knows how to find him out, take his feet, do not bother him, fear him, do not underestimate him.

113. Indeed, you cannot know the plans of Neter, you cannot perceive tomorrow.

114. Sit yourself at the hands of Neter, and your tranquillity will cause them to open.

115. Do not eat a meal in the presence of a magistrate, nor set to speaking first.

116. If you are satisfied with false words, enjoy yourself with your spittle.

117. Look at the cup in front of you, and let it suffice your need.

118. Even as a noble is important in his office, he is like the abundance of a well when it is drawn.

119. Do not listen to the accusation of an official indoors, and then repeat it to another outside.

120. Do not allow your discussions to be brought outside so that your heart will not be grieved.

121. The heart of a man is the beak of the Neter, so take care not to slight it.

122. A man who stands at the side of an official should not have his name known in the street.

123. Do not jeer at a blind man nor tease a dwarf, neither interfere with the condition of a cripple.

124. Do not taunt a man who is in the hand of Neter, nor scowl at him if he errs.
125. Man is clay and straw, and Neter is his potter.
126. He overthrows and he builds daily, he impoverishes a thousand if he wishes.
127. He makes a thousand into examiners, when he is in his hour of life.
128. How fortunate is he who reaches the West, when he is safe in the hand of Neter.
129. Do not stay in the tavern and join someone greater than you, whether he be high or low in his station, an old man or a youth.
130. But take as a friend for yourself someone compatible: Ra is helpful though he is far away.
131. When you see someone greater than you outside, and attendants following him, respect him.
132. And give a hand to an old man filled with beer: Respect him as his children would.
133. The strong arm is not weakened when it is uncovered.
134. The back is not broken when one bends it.
135. Better is the poor man who speaks sweet words, than the rich man who speaks harshly.
136. A pilot who sees into the distance will not let his ship capsize.
137. Do not reproach someone older than you, for he has seen the Sun before you.
138. Do not let yourself be reported to the Aten when he rises, with the words, "Another young man has reproached an elder."
139. Very sick in the sight of Ra is a young man who reproaches an elder.
140. Let him beat you with your hands folded, let him reproach you while you keep quiet. Then when

you come before him in the morning he will give you bread freely.

141. As for bread, he who has it becomes a dog, he barks to the one who gives it.

142. Do not expose a widow if you have caught her in the fields, nor fail to give way if she is accused.

143. Do not turn a stranger away from your oil jar that it may be made double for your family.

144. Neter loves him who cares for the poor, more than him who respects the wealthy.

145. Do not turn people away from crossing the river when you have room in your ferryboat.

146. If a steering oar is given you in the midst of the deep waters, bend back your hands to take it up.

147. It is not an abomination in the hand of Neter if the passenger is not cared for.

148. Do not acquire a ferryboat on the river, and then attempt to seek out its fares.

149. Take the charge from the man of means, but also accept the destitute without charge.

150. Mark for yourself these instructions: They please, they instruct, they are the foremost of all books.

151. They teach the ignorant.

152. If they are read to an ignorant man, he will be purified through them.

153. Seize them, put them in your mind and have men interpret them, explaining as a teacher.

154. As to a scribe who is experienced in his position, he will find himself worthy of being a courtier.

155. It is finished. By the writing of Senu, son of the Neter's father Pamiu.

Chapter 5

BOOK OF MERIKARA

Here begins the teaching which the King made for his son
Merikara.

1. Be skilful in speech, that you may be strong, it
is the strength of the tongue, and words are
braver than all fighting, none can circumvent the
clever man on the mat, a wise man is a school
for the magnates, and those who are aware of
his knowledge do not attack him. Falsehood does
not exist near him, but truth comes to him in full
essence, after the manner of what the Ancestors
said.

2. Copy your Ancestors, for work is carried out
through knowledge, see their words endure in
writing. Open, that you may read and copy
knowledge, even the expert will become one who
is instructed. Do not be evil, for patience is good.
Make your lasting monument in the love of you.
Multiply the people whom the city has enfolded,
then will Neter be praised because of rewards,
men will watch over you and give thanks for your
goodness, and your health will be prayed for.

3. Respect the great, keep your people safe. Consolidate your frontier and your patrolled area, for it is good to work for the future. Show respect for life for the clear-sighted, but the trusting man will suffer pain. Let men be sent to you through your kindly disposition. Wretched is he who has bound the land to himself and a fool is he who is greedy when others possess. Life on earth passes away, it is not long, he is fortunate who has a good remembrance in it. No man goes straight forward, even though a million belong to the Lord of the Two Lands. No one shall live forever. He who comes from the hand of Ausar shall depart, just as he who is self-indulgent shall be lost.

4. Make your magnates great, that they may execute your laws, one who is rich in his house will not be one-sided, for he who does not lack is an owner of property. A poor man does not speak truly, and one who says, "if only I had," is not straightforward, he is one-sided toward the possessor of rewards. Great is the great one whose great ones are great. Valiant is a king who owns an entourage, and august is he who is rich in magnates. Speak truth in your house, so that the magnates who are on earth may respect you, for a sovereign's reputation lies in straightforwardness. It is the front room of a house that inspires the back room with respect.

5. Do justice that you may live long upon earth. Calm the weeper, do not oppress the widow. Do not oust a man from his father's property. Do not degrade magnates from their seats. Beware of punishing wrongfully. Do not kill, for it will not profit you, but punish with beatings and with imprisonment, for thus the land will be set in

order, excepting only the rebel who has conspired, for Neter knows those who are disaffected, and Neter will smite down his evil doing with blood. The soul comes to the place which it knows, and it will not overstep the ways of the past, no Hekau can oppose it, and it will reach those who will give it water.

6. As for the tribunal which judges the needy, you know that they will not be lenient on that day of judging the poor, in the hour of exercising their function. Wretched is he who is accused as a wise man. Do not put your trust in length of years, for they regard a lifetime as an hour, a man survives after death, and his deeds are laid before him in a heap. Existence yonder is eternal, and he who complains of it is a fool, but as for him who attains it, he will be like a Neter yonder, striding forward like the lords of eternity.

7. Raise up your young troops, that the Residence may love you. Multiply your partisans as neighbours, see, your towns are full of newly settled folk. It is for twenty years that the rising generation is happy in following its desire, and neighbours come forth again. He who is caused to enter goes in for himself by means of children. Ancient times have fought for us, and I raised troops from them at my accession. Make your magnates great, promote your warriors. Increase the rising generation of your retainers, they must be equipped with knowledge, established with lands, and endowed with cattle.

8. Do not distinguish the son of a man of rank from a commoner, but take a man to yourself because of his actions, so that every craft may be carried on

for the possessor of strength. Guard your frontier. Marshal your fortresses, for troops are profitable to their master. Construct fine monuments to Neter, for it means the perpetuation of the name of whoever does it, and a man should do what is profitable to his soul, namely monthly service as priest and the wearing of white sandals. Enrich the fane, be discreet concerning the mysteries, enter into the sanctuary, eat bread in the temple, richly provide the altars, increase the revenues, add to the daily offerings, for it is a profitable matter for whoever does it. Maintain your monuments in proportion to your wealth, for a single day gives to eternity, an hour does well for the future, and Neter is aware of him who serves him. Dispatch your statues to a distant land of which they shall not render an inventory, for he who destroys the goods of an enemy will suffer.

9. You stand well with the Southern Region, for the bearers of loads come to you with produce. I did the same as the Ancestors, and there was none who had corn who gave it. Be kindly to those who are weak toward you, and satisfy yourself with your own bread and beer. Granite comes to you without hindrance, so do not destroy someone else's monuments. Hew stone in Tura, but do not build your tomb of what has been thrown down, or of what has been made for what is to be made. See, the king is a possessor of joy, you can be drowsy and you can sleep through your strength of arm, follow your desire through what I have done, for there is no enemy within your frontier.

10. Speak thus concerning the barbarian: As for the wretched Asiatic, unpleasant is the place where he

is, with trouble from water, difficulty from many trees, and the roads thereof awkward by reason of mountains. He does not dwell in one place, being driven hither and yonder through want, going about the desert on foot. He has been fighting since the time of Heru. He never conquers, yet he is not conquered, and he does not announce a day of fighting, like a thief whom a community has driven out.

11.   But I lived, and while I existed, the barbarians were as though in the walls of a fortress. My troops broke open. I caused the Delta to smite them, I carried off their people. I took away their cattle, until the detestation of the Asiatics was against Kamit. Do not worry about him, for the Asiatic is a crocodile on his riverbank. He snatches a lonely serf, but he will never rob in the vicinity of a populous town.

12.   The late King Akhtoy ordained in a teaching: "Be inactive about the violent man who destroys altars, for Neter will attack him who rebels against the temples. Men will come about it according as he does it, he will be satisfied with what is ordained for him, namely a trap for him. No one will use loyalty toward him on that day of coming, protect the altars, venerate Neter, and do not say: 'It is weakness of mind.'" Do not let your arms be loose. As for him who makes rebellion against you, it is to destroy the sky. Prosperity means a year of monuments, even if an enemy knows, he will not destroy them, through the desire that what he has done may be embellished by another who comes after. There is not one devoid of an enemy, but the ruler of the Two Banks is a wise man, and a king

who possesses an entourage cannot act stupidly. He is wise from birth, and Neter will distinguish him above millions of men.

13. The kingship is a goodly office. It has no son and it has no brother who shall make its monuments endure, yet it is the one person who ennobles the other. A man works for his predecessor, through the desire that what he has done may be embellished by another who shall come after him. A mean act was committed in my reign, and the territory of Thinis was devastated. It indeed happened, but not through what I had done. I knew of it only after it was done. See, the consequences exceeded what I had done, for what is damaged is spoiled, and there is no benefit for him who restores what he himself has ruined, who demolishes what he has built and embellished what he has defaced, beware of it! A blow is repaid by the like of it, and all that is achieved is a hitting.

14. One generation of men passes to another, and Neter, who knows character, has hidden himself. There is none who will oppose the possessor of a hand, and he is an attacker of what the eyes see, so venerate Neter upon his way. Things are made of costly stone and fashioned in copper. The mud flat is replaced with water. There is no stream that can be made to hide, for it means that the dike in which it hid itself is destroyed. The soul goes to the place it knows and does not stray on yesterday's road. Beautify your mansion in the West. Embellish your place in the Duat with straightforwardness and just dealing, for it is on that, which their hearts rely. More acceptable is

the character of the straightforward man than the ox of the wrongdoer.

15. Serve Neter, that he may do the like for you, with offerings for replenishing the altars and with carving. It is that which will show forth your name, and Neter is aware of whoever serves him. Provide for men, the cattle of Neter, for he made heaven and earth at their desire. He suppressed the greed of the waters. He gave the Breath of Life to their noses, for they are likeness of him which issued from his flesh. He shines in the sky for the benefit of their hearts. He has made herbs, cattle, and fish to nourish them. He has killed his enemies and destroyed his own children, because they had planned to make rebellion. He makes daylight for the benefit of their hearts, and he sails around in order to see them. He has raised up a shrine behind them, and when they weep, he hears. He has made them rulers even from the egg, a lifter to lift the load from the back of the weak man. He has made for them Hekau to be weapons to ward off what may happen.

16. Be watchful over it, by night as by day. How has he killed the disaffected? Even as a man strikes his son for his brother's sake, for Neter knows every name.

17. See, I have told you the best of my innermost thoughts, which you should set steadfastly before your face.

Chapter 6

BOOK OF DUA-KHETY

1. Here begins the teaching which the man of Tjel named Dua-Khety made for his son named Pepy, while he sailed southwards to the Residence to place him in the school of writings among the children of the magistrates, the most eminent men of the Residence.

2. So he spoke to him: Since I have seen those who have been beaten, it is to writings that you must set your mind. Observe the man who has been carried off to a work force. Behold, there is nothing that surpasses writings! They are a boat upon the water.

3. Read then at the end of the Book of Kemyet this statement in it saying: As for a scribe in any office in the Residence, he will not suffer want in it. When he fulfils the bidding of another, he does not come forth satisfied. I do not see an office to be compared with it, to which this maxim could relate. I shall make you love books more than your mother, and I shall place their excellence before you. It is greater than any office. There is nothing like it on earth. When he began to become sturdy but was still a child, he was greeted respectfully.

When he was sent to carry out a task, before he returned he was dressed in adult garments.

4. I do not see a stoneworker on an important errand or in a place to which he has been sent, but I have seen a coppersmith at his work at the door of his furnace. His fingers were like the claws of the crocodile, and he stank more than fish excrement.

5. Every carpenter who bears the blade is wearier than a fieldhand. His field is his wood, his hoe is the axe. There is no end to his work, and he must labour excessively in his activity. At night-time he still must light his lamp.

6. The jeweller pierces stone in stringing beads in all kinds of hard stone. When he has completed the inlaying of the eye-amulets, his strength vanishes and he is tired out. He sits until the arrival of the sun, his knees and his back bent at the place called Aku-Ra.

7. The barber shaves until the end of the evening. But he must be up early, crying out, his bowl upon his arm. He takes himself from street to street to seek out someone to shave. He wears out his arms to fill his belly, like bees that eat only according to their work.

8. The reed-cutter goes downstream to the Delta to fetch himself arrows. He must work excessively in his activity. When the mosquitoes sting him and the sand fleas bite him as well, then he is judged.

9. The potter is covered with earth, although his lifetime is still among the living. He burrows in the field more than swine to bake his cooking vessels. His clothes being stiff with mud, his head cloth consists only of rags, so that the air which comes forth from his burning furnace enters his

nose. He operates a pestle with his feet with which he himself is pounded, penetrating the courtyard of every house and driving earth into every open place.

10. I shall also describe to you the bricklayer. His kidneys are painful. When he must be outside in the wind, he lays bricks without a garment. His belt is a cord for his back, a string for his buttocks. His strength has vanished through fatigue and stiffness, kneading all his excrement. He eats bread with his fingers, although he washes himself but once a day.

11. It is miserable for the carpenter when he planes the roof-beam. It is the roof of a chamber 10 by 6 cubits. A month goes by in laying the beams and spreading the matting. All the work is accomplished. But as for the food which is to be given to his household while he is away, there is no one who provides for his children.

12. The vintner carries his shoulder-yoke. Each of his shoulders is burdened with age. A swelling is on his neck, and it festers. He spends the morning in watering leeks and the evening with corianders, after he has spent the midday in the palm grove. So it happens that he sinks down at last and dies through his deliveries, more than one of any other profession.

13. The fieldhand cries out more than the guinea fowl. His voice is louder than the raven's. His fingers have become ulcerous with an excess of stench. When he is taken away to be enrolled in the Delta labour, he is in tatters. He suffers when he proceeds to the island, and sickness is his payment. The forced labour then is tripled. If he

comes back from the marshes there, he reaches his house worn out, for the forced labour has ruined him.

14. The weaver inside the weaving house is more wretched than a woman. His knees are drawn up against his belly. He cannot breathe the air. If he wastes a single day without weaving, he is beaten with 50 whip lashes. He has to give food to the doorkeeper to allow him to come out to the daylight.

15. The arrow maker, completely wretched, goes into the desert. Greater than his own pay is what he has to spend for his ass for its work afterwards. Great is also what he has to give to the fieldhand to set him on the right road to the flint source. When he reaches his house in the evening, the journey has ruined him. The courier goes abroad after handing over his property to his children, being fearful of the lions and the Asiatics. He only knows himself when he is back in Kamit. But his household by then is only a tent. There is no happy homecoming.

16. The furnace-tender, his fingers are foul, the smell thereof is as corpses. His eyes are inflamed because of the heaviness of smoke. He cannot get rid of his dirt, although he spends the day at the reed pond. Clothes are an abomination to him.

17. The sandal maker is utterly wretched carrying his tubs of oil. His stores are provided with carcasses, and what he bites is hides.

18. The washerman launders at the riverbank in the vicinity of the crocodile. I shall go away, father, from the flowing water, said his son and his daughter, to a more satisfactory profession, one

more distinguished than any other profession. His food is mixed with filth, and there is no part of him which is clean. He cleans the clothes of a woman in menstruation. He weeps when he spends all day with a beating stick and a stone there. One says to him, dirty laundry, come to me, the brim overflows.

19. The fowler is utterly weak while searching out for the denizens of the sky. If the flock passes by above him, then he says: "Would that I might have nets." But Neter will not let this come to pass for him, for he is opposed to his activity.

20. I mention for you also the fisherman. He is more miserable than one of any other profession, one who is at his work in a river infested with crocodiles. When the totalling of his account is made for him, then he will lament. One did not tell him that a crocodile was standing there, and fear has now blinded him. When he comes to the flowing water, so he falls as through the might of Neter.

21. See, there is no office free from supervisors, except the scribe's. He is the supervisor!

22. But if you understand writings, then it will be better for you than the professions which I have set before you. Behold the official and the dependent pertaining to him. The tenant farmer of a man cannot say to him: "Do not keep watching me." What I have done in journeying southward to the Residence is what I have done through love of you. A day at school is advantageous to you. Seek out its work early, while the workmen I have caused you to know hurry on and cause the disobedient to hasten.

23. I will also tell you another matter to teach you what you should know at the station of your debating. Do not come close to where there is a dispute. If a man reproves you, and you do not know how to oppose his anger, make your reply cautiously in the presence of listeners.

24. If you walk to the rear of officials, approach from a distance behind the last. If you enter while the master of the house is at home, and his hands are extended to another in front of you, sit with your hand to your mouth. Do not ask for anything in his presence. But do as he says to you. Beware of approaching the table.

25. Be serious, and great as to your worth. Do not speak secret matters. For he who hides his innermost thoughts, is one who makes a shield for himself. Do not utter thoughtless words when you sit down with an angry man.

26. When you come forth from school after midday recess has been announced to you, go into the courtyard and discuss the last part of your lesson book.

27. When an official sends you as a messenger, then say what he said. Neither take away nor add to it.

28. He who abandons a chest of books, his name will not endure. He who is wise in all his ways, nothing will be hidden from him, and he will not be rebuffed from any station of his.

29. Do not say anything false about your mother. This is an abomination to the officials.

30. The offspring who does useful things, his condition is equal to the one of yesterday.

31. Do not indulge with an undisciplined man, for it is bad after it is heard about you. When you

have eaten three loaves of bread and swallowed two jugs of beer, and the body has not yet had enough, fight against it. But if another is satiated, do not stand, take care not to approach the table.

32. See, you send out a large number. You hear the words of the officials. Then you may assume the characteristics of the children of men, and you may walk in their footsteps.

33. One values a scribe for his understanding, for understanding transforms an eager person. You are to stand when words of welcome are offered. Your feet shall not hurry when you walk. Do not approach a trusted man, but associate with one more distinguished than you. But let you friend be a man of your generation.

34. See, I have placed you on the path of Neter. The fate of a man is on his shoulders on the day he is born. He comes to the judgement hall and the court of magistrates which the people have made. See, there is no scribe lacking sustenance, or the provisions of the royal house. It is Meskhenet who is turned toward the scribe who presents himself before the court of magistrates. Honour your father and mother who have placed you on the path of the living. Mark this, which I have placed before your eyes, and the children of your children.

35. It has come to an end in peace.

Chapter 7

BOOK OF KA-
KHEPERA-SENEB

The collection of words, the gathering of sayings, the pursuit of utterances with searching of heart, made by the priest of Heliopolis, Ka-Khepera-Seneb, called Onkhu. He says:

1. If I had unknown utterances, sayings that are unfamiliar, even new speech that has not occurred before, free from repetitions, not the utterance of what has long passed, which the Ancestors spoke. I squeeze out my breast for what is in it, in dislodging all that I say, for it is but to repeat what has been said when what has already been said has been said.

2. There is no support for the speech of the Ancestors when the descendants find it dry. I have spoken this in accordance with what I have seen, beginning with the first men down to those who shall come after. If I might know what others have not known, even what has not been repeated, that I might speak them and that my heart might answer me, that I might make clear to it, my

heart concerning my ill, that I might throw off the burden that is on my back.

3. I am meditating on the things that have happened, the events that have occurred in the land. Transformations go on. It is not like last year. One year is more burdensome than the next. Righteousness is cast out. Iniquity is in the midst of the council-hall. The plans of the Neteru are violated, their dispositions are disregarded. The land is in distress, mourning is in every place, towns and districts are in lamentation. All men alike are under wrongs. As for respect, an end is made of it.

4. The lords of quiet are disquieted. A morning comes every day and turned back again to what has been. When I would speak, my limbs are heavy laden. I am distressed because of my heart. It is suffering to hold my peace concerning it. Another heart would bow down, but a brave heart in distress is the companion of its lord. If I had a heart able to suffer, then would I rest in it. I would load it with words of joy, that I might dislodge through it my malady.

5. He said to his heart: Come then my heart, that I may speak to thee, and that thou may answer for me my sayings, and may you explain to me that which is in the land. I am meditating on what has happened. Calamities come in today, tomorrow afflictions are not past. All men are silent concerning it, although the land is in great disturbance. Nobody is free from evil. All men alike do it. Hearts are sorrowful. He who gives commands is as he to whom commands are given. The heart of both of them is content. Men awake

to it in the morning daily, but hearts thrust it not away.

6. The fashion of yesterday therein, is like today and resembles it. There is none so wise that he perceives and none so angry that he speaks. Men awake in the morning to suffer every day. Long and heavy is my malady. The poor man has no strength to save himself from him that is stronger than he. It is painful to keep silent concerning the things heard, but it is suffering to reply to the ignorant man. To criticise an utterance causes enmity, for the heart receives not the truth, and the reply to a matter is not endured. All that a man desires is his own utterance.

7. I speak to thee, my heart, answer thou me, for a heart assailed is not silent. Lo, the affairs of the servant are like those of the master. Manifold is the burden upon thee.

BOOK OF HORDEDEF

1. Find fault with yourself, before another person does.
2. If you want excellence, establish a household with a strong wife and children.
3. Beautify your house and make excellence your place.
4. Although death is bitter, life is exalted, and the house of death is for life.

BOOK OF AANKHU

1. Silence is sacred.
2. Learn to be quiet so you can really hear.
3. Learn to be quiet so you can really see.
4. In Silence All can be heard.
5. In Silence All can be known.
6. As our Ancestors would say, "For Knowledge, Know that Peace is an indispensable condition in attaining it."
7. The inner most Self speaks in silence, its Wisdom resounds in tranquillity.
8. Learn to be still, so you can hear it.
9. Learn to be still so you can listen.
10. Learn to be still, so it can guide you.
11. Stillness is crucial to moving with the Divine, for the resonance of its silence carries the still man to freedom.
12. Silence is sacred.
13. Cherish the silence.
14. To interrupt its speech, one should have a good reason otherwise they create the greatest of blasphemies.
15. Speak not if your words do not soothe.
16. Speak not, if your words do not heal.
17. Speak not, if your words do not enlighten.

18. Speak not if your words do not delight.
19. Speak not, if your words do not move the hearer towards stillness.
20. If your words do not still, speak not, let the silence live.
21. In silence, one communes with the Divine.
22. In silence, one transcends space and time.
23. In silence one comes to eternity.
24. In silence, one touches immortality.
25. Silence is Divinity itself.
26. Learn to be silent.
27. Still the heart that you may walk in joy.
28. Still the heart that you may walk in peace.
29. Still the heart that you may live righteously.
30. Keep the heart light, that your life may be a blessing.
31. Keep the heart light, that you may live long.
32. Keep the heart light so Neter can use you.
33. The heavy heart cannot know joy, all it knows is its burden.
34. The heavy heart cannot know peace, all it knows is its burden.
35. The heavy heart cannot live righteously for it tips the scales of truth.
36. The heavy heart is discarded, for Neter cannot use it.
37. Open the heart, and release your burden.
38. Open the heart, and let Neter in.
39. Open the heart, and let the light shine through, dispelling all darkness.
40. Open the heart that the breath of life may air out the staleness.
41. Open the heart, to make way for the new.
42. Empty the heart, that it may be full with joy.
43. Empty the heart, that it may be full with peace.
44. Empty the Heart that it may be full of love.

45. You will find fulfilment, when you empty the heart.
46. Man is the definition of Neter, however, the further man defines the Self, the further he confines and restrains Neter.
47. Beware of allowing your ego to oppress you with an overwhelming sense of purpose.
48. This stems from a sense of lack and discontentment.
49. What one is feeling is a void, but makes the mistake of thinking it is outer.
50. This void is the eternal internal, it is the Self.
51. Therefore, look no further than yourself for fulfilment, and strive towards the inner.
52. When you find the inner, the outer will be there waiting for you.
53. What is happening is not as important as to its meaning in the grand scheme of things.
54. Look beyond the surface.
55. Which Neter is speaking to you? That is really reading and understanding Metu Neter.
56. Disgrace your Shepsu and the very blood within your veins will become a curse to you.
57. The seed of Neter rests at the very core of your Being.
58. It is the Self which has infinite potential and infinite possibilities.
59. Make your very reason for living its cultivation and realization.
60. Potential unrealized and not actualized begins to ferment and decay. It breeds corruption and corrodes away at the inner essence.
61. When this happens, Ausar himself becomes the very demon that haunts the temple. This is why we Nehem Neter. Open the Sarcophagus, and free the Neter within.

62. Always maintain command of your Attention.
63. Give your Attention away foolishly and you've sold your Self into bondage.
64. The spiritually immature and those who choose the darkness seek to distract the righteous with irrelevant concepts and carnal images.
65. Therefore, master the art of ignoring, and be conservative with your Attention. This will make you wise.
66. If one wishes to master the Self they must become the master of their Attention.
67. As Neter, your must remember that the Neteru are your limbs.
68. Master your members or they will master you.
69. What a sad sight it is to see children oppress their parents.
70. There is only **One Being** in existence, and everything is a manifestation of that **One Being**.
71. This **One Being** is Neter.
72. Therefore it is good to remind one's Self of this one thing. I alone exist.
73. Every day you are as Ra, Rising from the Waters of Nu, giving birth to a new creation.
74. Purify in the Waters of Nu daily, hourly, by the minute.
75. There is healing in those waters.
76. Don't even allow the filth of three minutes ago to remain on you.
77. Pert Em Hru means to live in the now.
78. Be present, this is the secret of immortality.
79. The Initiate that wishes to enter into the Sekhet-Hetepu must not wait to die.
80. They must go to meet death. Embrace It!
81. In embracing death, the Initiate will find true life.

82. Sit upon the throne of Seker and offer Het-Heru your rebellious head. In return she will offer you the Shekhem staff and this world will become your Field of Offerings, your Garden of Peace.

83. As Heru redeemed the work of Ausar, we must work to redeem our Ancestors. This is Nehem Neter.

84. You are the most important book that you can ever read, you are the secret scroll that must unfold, and you are the deepest mystery that you can ever penetrate. Delve into the Divine Mysteries of You!

85. To be a Neter, is to be able to create simply through the word.

86. By simply speaking, making a decree, a Neter causes what she wills to come into being.

87. The enlightened person eventually goes on to become a Star, a Yakhu, a light being.

88. Ra's chief symbol is the sun.

89. However, Ra is not the sun, he is the source of energy, light and life itself.

90. Het-Heru is the medium through which Ra brings creation into being.

91. We are the Original People of the Earth.

Chapter 10

BOOK OF MERI

1. One who drinks from the wisdom of his Ancestors will never be led astray by fools.
2. A husband will be twice bound if his chains feel comfortable.
3. Bathe her with perfumed water, and then fill her heart with music and sweet words.
4. If you marry a monkey for his wealth, when the money goes, the monkey will remain as is.
5. The woman who does not covet the possessions of her husband is in love with another man.
6. If you are wise, look after your home and love your wife without holding back.
7. One who marries for love alone will always have good nights even on bad days.
8. Two hearts that beat as one, send signals to each other in whispers.
9. Marry the heart not the body, for the body changes with age, and never returns.
10. Every man must act in the rhythm of his own time, such is wisdom. Pace thyself.
11. Even sweet-smelling roses have thorns.
12. A muse is there to inspire and amuse your life-force, not to suck it dry.

13. Touch the animal and see how she moves.
14. A woman's ruin lies in her tongue.
15. Tiny steps bring about lasting change.
16. A lemon shared with a friend tastes like an orange.
17. A loyal, peaceful and joyful wife is a blessing from the Ancestors, appreciate her as such.
18. Borrowing money is hardship, because paying it back is always a loss.
19. Making money by selling garbage is better than losing money selling fine silk.
20. Tut-ankh-amen. She is the living image of the hidden Neter.
21. Becoming requires overcoming.
22. If your heart could speak, you would know you are Neter.
23. It's a thin line between faith and insanity.
24. Some people are filled with admiration and reverence when they hear evil words and deeds.
25. If you're a genius at something, never do it for free.
26. If you have to drag a dog to the hunt, neither he nor his hunting is any good.
27. If it weren't for darkness, light would not exist.
28. Our children's children are just as precious as our own children.
29. Wait for the heart to calm down before you dare open your mouth.
30. Our children are proof of our Immortality.
31. We built pyramids, period, we are Neteru.
32. Stroke his ego and see how he always comes back for more.
33. Run as hard as a wild beast if you will, but you won't get any reward greater than that destined for you.

34. Silence is the best answer to the stupid.
35. Fools are stepping-stones of the wise.
36. Bitter hearts always find something to cry about, even in the presence of Neter's beauty.
37. Around every corner, always protect the engine that powers you.
38. None but the pure must approach the pure.
39. The Ego is selfish but the Soul is self-centred.
40. The purpose of life is evolution.
41. You exist to manifest the full potential of the hidden intelligence within you.
42. Guard your words with all your might and make sure they serve your purpose.
43. Each year of your life must be marked by a major project which you accomplish, sooner or later, you will build your own pyramid.
44. See no evil. Hear no evil. Think no evil. Do no evil.
45. You are never alone, tax, interest, and administration fees are everywhere you go.
46. Money is a Force of Nature, if you treat her well she multiplies, if you don't she will find a suitable master.
47. Faith and deception are identical twins.
48. Metu Neter is the language of Creation itself.
49. To know truth you must seek proof. Proof comes through experimentation or sound logic.
50. She who understands music, groks the cosmos.
51. The child has faith in fairy tales, but the elder knows truth.
52. A hunter in search of an elephant does not stop to throw stones at birds.
53. The sun came before the moon, and gave birth to its Children. The Children of the Moon came

after, and continue to steal light from the Children of the Sun, because they have no light of their own. Only time will take care of the Children of the Moon.

54. When evil runs out of the good to fight, it turns on itself.

55. There is no Forgiveness without Justice.

56. Only your enemy benefits from you turning the other cheek.

57. The sun will shine on those who stand before those who kneel.

58. There is a time for war and a time for peace, wisdom is knowing what time it is.

59. Because we focused on the snake, we missed the scorpion.

60. If you happen to visit the house of a liar, believe him up to the door of his house but no further than that.

61. History is a compass and a clock that tells us where we are and what time it is as a people.

62. Give the minimum time you need to make it in the world of your enemy, but reserve the best and most of your time to creating your own world, according to your own understanding and vision of your life.

63. Dream your own dreams, open your own eyes, and see the world through the eyes of your African Ancestors, the Eye of Heru, which saw the universe as a living being.

64. Freedom of speech is only valid if it agrees with Maat and benefits the whole village.

65. Patience is a virtue only if it advances your cause.

66. Even small, slow and steady drops can fill a bathtub.

67. At the end of the day, after all the endless arguments, Maat wins!
68. Maat is organisation, only a fool tries to lead people without the knowledge of Maat.
69. Follow your heart once it has been purified.
70. Many are born with worms in their spirits, the Way of Maat allows us to exorcise them.
71. Attention is worth more than gold, spend it wisely and you will realise the Neter within.
72. Everything we experience comes from within.
73. Blood makes you a relative but loyalty makes you family.
74. The Language of the Neteru is only learned by those who seek to cultivate it in earnest.
75. The Universe exists only for the Creator to experience and know itself as Creator.
76. There is no limit to the infinite ability of the Neter within.
77. Imagination and Trance are the key to unlocking the infinite potential of the Neter within.
78. Emotions are there to serve you, not to rule you.
79. The Will is empowered to manifest itself in the world by Imagination and Trance.
80. Man is made up of Intelligence and Power, the Intelligence must lead and the Power must follow. Disorders manifest when the roles are reversed.
81. When you awaken the Neter within, you become like the Sun with your own solar system.
82. The present never ends. You live in the present. Stop worrying about the past or the future.
83. The lifepath of a Heru is paved with synchronicity and convergence.
84. To experience eternity, you must live in the moment!

85. Immortality is a state of Awareness, that is achieved when we start thinking totally in the present, without thinking of the past or the future.

86. What we do during the day visits us at night in our dreams.

87. To change your life, change the images and sounds that surround you, to suit your new purpose.

88. The Universe is Ancestral.

89. Cash is king, debt is slavery.

90. Your mind is a mirror, guard against what it sees, and what it hears.

91. Even in good food, drink and company, a miserable heart finds no joy.

92. There's no substitute for strategy and careful planning.

93. Structure follows strategy.

94. It is not good enough to teach wisdom to men using only words, one must inject it directly into their blood.

95. Opportunity is found in unsolved problems.

96. The pyramids are a timeless billboard of African genius.

97. Evolution is the unfolding of the potential of the hidden intelligence within.

98. Elevation requires separation from the sleeping masses.

99. He let the beautiful girl come into his heart, but along with her came the worms in her spirit.

100. Having the backing of the Ancestors is more powerful than the support of any army.

101. If I Die, Neter Dies!

Chapter 11

BOOK OF NEBT HET

1. Always keep the main house loved, respected, and protected.
2. Never replace the main house with the second house.
3. Maintain surplus resources for all the houses, without fail.

Chapter 12

BOOK OF IMHOTEP

1. When I was a very young boy, my father Kanefer, and mother Khreduonkh, placed me under the tutelage of a great African Priest of the Nile, from Annu, who taught me everything that I eventually knew and mastered.

2. I became an architect who built one of the first pyramids in Kamit. I also became a doctor, priest, scribe, sage, poet, astrologer, vizier and chief minister for the Nesu Djoser. I was supervisor of everything in this entire land of Kamit.

3. I controlled the departments of the Judiciary, Treasury, War, Interior, Agriculture, and the General Executive. I advised the Nesu in both spiritual and practical matters.

4. My position was also commonly referred to as "supervisor of that which Heaven brings, the Earth creates and the Nile brings."

5. Only the best educated and multi-skilled citizen could handle the range of duties associated with serving the Nesu of Kamit as vizier.

6. Because of my mastery of various skills, I was called by many names, "Chancellor of the Nesu of Lower Kamit," "Foremost under the Nesu,"

"Administrator of the Great House," "Hereditary Noble," "High Priest of Annu," "Chief Sculptor," "Bringer of the Nile Inundation," and "Chief Carpenter."

7. In my lifetime, I worked as architect and master builder of numerous projects because of the many blessings I received from the Shepsu and Neteru.

8. I codified the engineering lessons I had received by authoring the "Book of the Order of a Temple." It was an encyclopedia of architecture that was meant to be consulted by the builders of Kamit, and also by many generations down the line, after my death.

9. Through commitment, grit and drive I learned all that my teacher, father and mother taught me. I practised hard and deliberately all that was instructed to me. I was a quick study and hard-worker.

10. I also read all the words and teachings of the past African sages of Kamit, Nubia, Ethiopia and Punt, and studied closely their work.

11. But what made my coursework even easier to grok was the lessons I learned from the Neteru and the Shepsu themselves.

12. These I got by setting up and maintaining their shrines as instructed to me by my teacher. I took exact notes and never missed a chance to make daily hesi to the shrines.

13. This practice awoke and activated within me the many talents that the Neteru gifted to me. Because of their instructions I became a "Renaissance Man."

14. The advice from my teacher guided me towards really embracing the art and science of invocation of the Shepsu and the Neteru.

15. The Shepsu showed me the herbs to use for healing sick people. On the other hand, the Neteru also revealed unto me the many Hekau that I could employ to hone my craft and amass great power.

16. Through their guidance I could provide remedies for all diseases, and give sons to the childless.

17. By working closely with the Neter Ptah, I was able to harness his great power and great wisdom. It was as if I could see the Hekau that hold the universe together. I could read the blueprint and manipulate it to great benefit for the African nation of Kamit.

18. I became one with Ptah and he expressed himself through my Khat. This helped Kamit very much, as the talents I activated within could then be used to bestow many gifts upon the people of Kamit. From then onwards, some even started referring to me as, "Son of Ptah."

19. Thus the purpose of life was achieved, for the Creator could express itself as creator through me. Form and function were in harmony. Maat ruled my being.

20. The precepts found in the Book of Maat helped me cultivate discipline and order in my life from a very young age. My teacher and parents taught me that Maat, if practised daily, would enable my spirit to avoid Isfet, and be in harmony with the Forces of Nature.

21. Neb-er-tcher stated it for a practical reason when he declared that, "My children invoke my name, and they overthrow their enemies. They make Hekau for the overthrowing of Apep."

22. The ancient African traditions instilled a sense of honour, victory, confidence, strength, courage and wisdom that allowed me to achieve so much.

23. Consequently, the Shepsu and Neteru guided me in the wisdom of the spirit, Hekau, formulation of medicine, and revealing the secrets of architecture and the universe.

24. All of this knowledge, intelligence and power came from them, as I was an astute and disciplined scholar, who loved receiving private instruction from them.

25. I dreamt. I explored. I created.

26. Relentless application of ritual and meditation were the key technology through which I could connect with these divine Forces of Nature, which are within and all around us.

27. It was by neither miracle nor senseless faith, but by proven science, hardwork and dedication to the ancient ways of our African Ancestors.

28. These are the keys that allowed me to open the secret gates to the sacred wisdom of the universe.

29. Follow my instructions without fail, and you too shall reap the great rewards that come with venerating the Shepsu and the Neteru.

30. May the Shepsu be with you!

Chapter 13

BOOK OF ANKHSHESHONK

1. Those who say: 'That can't happen' should take a look at what is hidden.
2. Every day Neter reveals the secrets of its creation on the Earth.
3. Neter created the light and the darkness in which all creation exists.
4. Your life runs true when heart and words are without fault.
5. Do not ask Neter for advice and then disregard it.
6. Do not teach those who do not want to hear a matter when a more important one awaits.
7. Do not let a fool intervene in an important matter or you will then have to appeal to a Sage.
8. When a wise man is put to the test he is hardly conscious of his spiritual achievements.
9. He who has been chosen out of the crowd is not automatically a wise man because of that.
10. Do not throw a spear if your aim is poor.
11. Do not allow the ignorant man and the fool to do work for which they are unsuited.

12. Do not say: "I have ploughed the field but haven't been paid in return."
13. Plough it again, it's good to work.
14. Never let an unwise or a mediocre man give orders to people.
15. Neter leaves town when it is governed by a bad ruler.
16. When Ra, the divine light, is absent in a country, law, justice and values break down and fools take the place of wise men.
17. If a woman is at peace with her husband, things will never go wrong.
18. When a man smells pleasantly of myrrh, his wife is like a cat before him.
19. But when a man is hurt, his wife is there like a lioness to protect him.
20. Do not dwell in a house that has been abandoned by the Ancestors (Amadlozi). Its capacity for destruction will turn on you.
21. Do not say "I know," rather put yourself to learn.
22. Do not scorn a little thing, for it has the power to make you suffer. A little worry can break your back, a little good news can make your heart leap, a little dew can make the grass live, a little bee can make honey.
23. The riches of the generous man are greater than those of the miser.
24. Those who like to give food to others will find welcome at every table in every house.
25. Do not neglect to help those who help you.
26. The wealth of a city is a righteous governor.
27. The wealth of a temple is a good priest.
28. The wealth of a field is the time when the land is worked.

29. The wealth of a store is when goods are stocked.
30. The wealth of a home is a wise woman.
31. The wealth of a sage is his words.
32. The wealth of a workman is his tools.
33. Acquiring things with greed is an evil that has no end.
34. It is greed that leads to quarrels and fighting in a household and brings unhappiness to families.
35. The rewards of greed are as ash blown on the wind.
36. He who spits at the Ancestors, his spit will fall back down on him.
37. Keep your distance from those with hate in their hearts.
38. The death of an evil man is a cause for celebration for those he leaves behind.
39. Everyone can find the path to the Ancestors, but fools cannot. For fools, the work of the Ancestors is nothing but a joke.
40. Advice given to the stupid weighs as little as the wind.
41. The fool who lights a fire gets too close and burns himself.
42. It is better to have a serpent hanging around the house than a fool.
43. The wicked acts of a fool harm those closest to him.
44. You exhaust a donkey by loading it with bricks.
45. Do not pamper yourself when you are young. Otherwise when you are old you will be weak.
46. Acknowledge the Ancestors so that you may be protected.
47. Serve your brothers and sisters that you may enjoy a good reputation.
48. Serve a wise person that he or she may serve you.

49. Serve one who serves you.

50. Serve any person so you may benefit from it.

51. And serve your mother and father that you may go forward and prosper.

52. Examine every matter so that you may understand it.

53. Do not say I am learned but rather set yourself to become wise.

54. Be gentle and patient, then your character will be beautiful.

55. It is in the development of character that instruction succeeds.

56. Learn the structure and functioning of the sky.

57. Learn the structure and functioning of the earth.

58. The good fortune of a country is a leader who acts righteously.

59. The good fortune of a temple is its priest.

60. The good fortune of a field is the time it is worked.

61. The good fortune of a storehouse is the stocking of it.

62. And the good fortune of the wise is their excellent advice.

63. May the elder brother of the town be the one to whom it is entrusted.

64. May the kindest brother of the family be the one who acts as elder brother for it.

65. May I have something and my relatives have something, so that I may eat my own without worrying.

66. May the floodwater never fail to come.

67. May the field never fail to flourish.

68. May children do honour to their father and mother.

69. May the moon follow the sun and not fail to rise.

70. May I recognize my friends that I may share my goods with them.
71. May I recognize my brother and sister that I may open my heart to them.
72. And may life always follow death.
73. Do not send a wise man in a small matter when an important matter is waiting.
74. Happy is the heart of him who has made a judgment before a wise man.
75. A wise master who asks for advice, his house stands forever.
76. A wise man seeks a friend, a fool seeks an enemy.
77. The children of a fool wander in the street, but those of the wise are always with them.
78. A wise man is one who knows what goes on around him.
79. May the heart of a wife be the heart of her husband so that they may be free of contention.
80. If a woman is at peace with her man, they will never fare badly.
81. If a woman whispers about her man, they will never fare well.
82. A good woman or man of noble character is food that comes in times of hunger.
83. A woman who remains a woman at night is praised during the day.
84. He who violates a married woman on the bed will have his wife violated on the ground.
85. Do not send a fool in an important matter when you can send one who is wise.
86. Do not instruct a fool lest he hate you for it.
87. When one instructs a fool, he or she says "What they are doing insults me."
88. The friend of a fool is a fool.

89. The friend of a wise person is another wise person.
90. If you are given bread for being stupid, you may learn to despise wisdom.
91. Although the way of the Ancestors is before all people, the fool cannot find it.
92. Do not belittle the elderly in your heart.
93. Honour the elderly in your heart, and you will be honoured in the hearts of all.
94. Do not laugh at your son in front of his mother lest you learn the measure of his father.
95. Do not prefer one of your children to the other, for you know not which one of them will be kind to you.
96. There is no tooth that decays and stays in its place.
97. There is no friend who walks alone.
98. There is no wise one who comes to grief.
99. There is no fool who finds profit.
100. There is no one who deserts his traveling companion whom the Ancestors do not hold accountable for it.
101. There is no one who deceives who is not deceived.
102. And there is no one who does wrong that goes on and truly prospers.
103. Do not hurl a lance if you cannot aim correctly.
104. Do not do evil to a person and thus cause another to do it to you.
105. Let your generosity reach one who needs it.
106. Do not be stingy, for wealth is no real security.
107. Speak truth to everyone, let it cling to your speech.
108. Do not do to a person what you dislike and thus cause another to do it to you also.
109. There is no good deed except the good deed that is done for one who needs it.
110. Those who struggle together with the people of their town will rejoice in the victory with them.

111. Do not go to court against your superior when you do not have protection against him.
112. Do not take yourself a woman whose husband is alive, lest he become your enemy.
113. In straight times or happy times wealth grows because of spreading it.
114. May your fate not be the fate of one who begs and is given.
115. When you work the land do not pamper your body.
116. Do not become distressed over possessions.
117. Do not become distressed over your occupation.
118. Do not become distressed over a matter if it is not going to kill you.
119. Do not go into hiding when you have no food to last you.
120. Do not act overly familiar with the one who is greater than you, lest he sees it as disrespect.
121. Do not be hasty when you speak, lest you offend.
122. Do not say at once that which comes to your heart, think about it twice before you open your mouth.
123. Your best interest is in inquiring.
124. You should enquire of three wise men about an individual matter if it is important enough for an oracular petition of the great Ancestors.
125. Do good for your body during your good days.
126. There is no one who does not die.
127. Whether times are constrained or times are joyful, property multiplies by spreading it.
128. The blessing of property is in a wise woman.
129. The blessing of an army is in a general.
130. The blessing of a wise man is in his mouth.
131. The blessing of a craftsman is in his equipment.

132. Do not despise a remedy that you regularly use.
133. Do not despise a matter of the King.
134. The one who frequently despises a thing, dies from it.
135. Do not quarrel over a matter in which you are wrong.
136. Do not dwell in a house with your in-laws.
137. Do not be a neighbour to your master.
138. More beautiful is the face of the one who has come up from the farmland, than that of the one who has spent the day in the town.
139. Do not put your wealth in a single place.
140. Do not incur expenses when you have not established your storehouse.
141. You should incur expenses in accordance with what you have.
142. A crocodile does not die of gladness, it is of hunger that it dies.
143. You may stumble with your foot in the house of a great man, you should not stumble with your tongue.
144. If you are thrown out of the house of your master, become his door-keeper.
145. Do not often be a hindrance, lest you be cursed.
146. Do not often get drunk, lest you be mad.
147. Do not kill a snake and leave its tail.
148. The character of a man is in his family.
149. The character of a man is in his association.
150. The character of a man is on his face.
151. You will say: "A good destiny" at the end of old age, but not before.
152. Put your affairs in the hands of the Ancestors.
153. Do not entrust your people to one who has not experienced distress.

154. Do not create your amusement out of one who is being distressed.

155. A man does not know his days of misery.

156. A wise master who asks, his house is established forever.

157. Happy is the heart of the one who has established judgement in the presence of a wise man.

158. Disdain ruins the great man.

159. Do not seek revenge. Do not cause revenge to be sought against you.

160. Do not undertake a matter that you will not be able to do.

161. Do not speak in a forceful voice to a man when you will not be able to intimidate him by it.

162. Do not say a thing when it is not its proper time.

163. The companion of a fool is a fool.

164. The companion of a wise man is a wise man.

165. Every man acquires property. It is the wise man who knows how to secure it.

166. If you find your wife with her lover, take for yourself a bride on the basis of worthiness.

167. Do not acquire for yourself two voices.

168. Speak truth to every man. Let it be inherent in your speech.

169. Do not open your heart to your secret lover. What you have said to her belongs to the street.

170. Do not take yourself a youth as a companion.

171. Do not take yourself a thief as a companion, lest he cause that you be killed.

172. The one who is stubborn in a bad matter eventually discovers its harm.

173. The one who robs the property of another does not discover its profit.

174. If you should be the companion of a wise man whose heart you do not know, do not open your mouth to him.
175. At night a thief steals, at noon he is found.
176. Do not multiply your words unnecessarily.
177. It is to the one who has property in his hand that a house is open.
178. A man who looks in front of himself does not stumble and fall.
179. Do not abandon a woman of your house when she does not become pregnant or give birth.
180. Do not cast an eye at the property of another, lest you become poor.
181. Do not fail to do the thing that your master has commanded specifically to you.
182. There is no good deed except a good deed that you have done for him who has need for it.
183. A man who has acquired his first money, its expenditure consists of drinking it and eating it.
184. Do not be afraid to do that which you are in the right.
185. More pleasing is dumbness than hastiness of the tongue.
186. More pleasing is sitting than doing a trivial errand.
187. Do not say: "I undertook this matter," when you did not undertake it.
188. Anger should not command you.
189. Greed will not give you the golden goose.
190. If you are sent after chaff and you find wheat, do not buy it.
191. Do not do what you hate to a man so as to cause another to do it to you.
192. One hundred men are killed because of one moment of distress.

193. Do not associate with a man who is disheartened and says: "It is just one moment of distress that I have."
194. Do not go to your brother when you are distressed. You should go to your friend.
195. Do not drink water in the house of a merchant. He will charge you for it.
196. Zealous service repels hatred.
197. Do not borrow money at interest to live in grand style by means of it.
198. Borrow money at interest to buy farmland.
199. Do not swear falsely when you are in distress, lest you fare worse than your current condition.
200. Do not speak of an important matter during beer.
201. Do not conceal yourself from a stranger who has come from abroad.
202. Do not lend money at interest without security in your hand.
203. Do not be too trusting, lest you become a poor man.
204. Do not despise a minor document, a small flame, or a subordinate soldier.
205. Do not take liberties with a woman when her husband is listening to your voice.
206. Do not be ashamed to do the work by which you will be able to live.
207. Do not acquire property when you do not have a storehouse.
208. Do not accept a gift when you will not make a contract.
209. Do not say: "My illness has gone away. I shall not use a remedy."
210. Do not go on the road without a stick in your hand.
211. Do not walk alone at night.

212. Do not scorn your master before a lesser man.
213. If you associate with a man and you are on good terms with him, if he fares badly, do not abandon him.
214. Inventory your house each and every hour that you may find its thief.
215. Teach your sons and daughters to write, to plough, to fish and to trap because of a year of withdrawn and inundation, and they will find the profit in what they have done.
216. Take dung, take manure, but do not make an occupation of scavenging.
217. Do not often relate matters in the presence of your master.
218. Be small in anger and your respect will be great in the hearts of all men.
219. If a gardener acts as a fisherman, his trees will perish.
220. Better is noble failure than half success.
221. Give 100 pieces of silver to a wise woman. Do not accept 200 pieces of silver from a foolish one.
222. He who hides behind his master will acquire 100 masters.
223. A man who has no town, his character serves as his family.
224. Take a great man to your home, take a lesser man to your boat.
225. Sweeter is the water of the one who has given it, than the wine of the one who has received it.
226. If an incompetent man repents, he will become a wise man.
227. A man does not love the one who hates him.
228. Do a good deed and throw it into the flood. When it subsides you will find it.

229. If two brothers quarrel, do not come between them.
230. He who comes between two brothers when they quarrel is placed between them when they are at peace.
231. There is no poor man except him who has died.
232. Do not be fainthearted when you are ill and never beg for death.
233. He who lives, his herbage grows.
234. It is a wise man who understands what passes before him.
235. Give your voice with your property, that it may make two gifts.
236. A remedy is good only in the hand of its physician.
237. If it is for incompetence that you are given bread, learning will be an abomination to you.
238. In the hands of the Founding Ancestors is all good fortune.
239. More important is the hissing of a snake than the braying of a donkey.
240. There is running to which sitting is preferable.
241. There is sitting to which standing is preferable.
242. Do not dwell in a house that is haunted. Death does not say: "I have come."
243. A serpent that is eating has no venom.
244. All manner of beasts are welcome in a house. A thief is not.
245. The approach of a fool means fleeing from him.
246. Exalt in your heart the men who are elders, that you may be exalted in the hearts of all men.
247. It is in accordance to the character of her husband that a woman allows herself to be seduced.
248. The waste of a house is in not dwelling in it.
249. The waste of a spouse is in not knowing them carnally.

250. The waste of a donkey is in carrying bricks.
251. The waste of a boat is in carrying straw.
252. There is no one who insults his superior, who is not himself the one insulted.
253. There is no one who employs deceit who is not deceived.
254. He who is ashamed to have sex with his wife, no children are borne to him.
255. Better a statue of stone than a foolish son.
256. Better death than greed.
257. Do not set a fire when you will not be able to extinguish it.
258. The one who shakes the stone, it is on his foot that it falls.
259. He who loves a woman on the street, the side of his purse is split open.
260. If a woman loves a crocodile, she takes on its character.
261. Do not speak ill of a beloved woman.
262. Do not speak praise of a hated woman.
263. For a fool to go about with a wise man is for a goose to go about with its butcher and knife.
264. A fool in a house is like clothing in a storehouse for wine.
265. If you are hungry, eat what you abominate. If you are full, abominate it.
266. If you are about to say something before your master, count on your hand up to ten.
267. Give one loaf to the one who does the labour, give two to the one who gives commands.
268. Killing does not occur without Neter knowing.
269. Nothing occurs except what Neter will allow.
270. Silence hides incompetence.
271. Do not desire a woman who has a husband.

272. He who desires a woman who has a husband, it is on her doorstep that he is killed.
273. It is better to dwell in your own small house than to dwell in the great house of another.
274. Small property intact is better than large property despoiled.
275. A slip of the tongue in the palace is a slip of the rudder at sea.
276. A male ox does not cry out to the calf.
277. The path of the Ancestors is before all men and women. The troublemaker does not find it.
278. Do not be energized in every sort of work and so be lazy in your own work.
279. He who is not lazy for his father, the father will be energetic for him.
280. Do not put the poor man in the presence of a rich man.
281. Do not drink water from a well and then throw the pitcher into it.
282. Do not make an unhappy woman your wife.
283. Man is better than a donkey at copulating, it is his purse that restrains him.
284. No drunkenness of yesterday halts the thirst of today.
285. Better to scavenge in hunger than to die in need.
286. If you are infuriated with your master, do not say to him the full extent of your heart.
287. When a town is in the process of beginning, go into it.
288. When a town is in the process of destruction, leave from it.
289. Do not take control of a matter whose ending you will not be able to control.

290. A good woman of character is as sustenance come forth during hunger.

291. There is no profit in a son whom you shall not find fit to reward.

292. There is no profit in a servant who will not do work.

293. There is no profit in a brother who will not care for you.

294. If a woman is at peace with her husband, it is the influence of the Ancestors.

295. Do not sell your house and your endowment in exchange for one day, and so be a poor man forever.

296. Do not seize a poor man from the property of the King, lest he destroy you and your family.

297. Do not take an unhappy person's words to your heart.

298. A person of low character is a fungus who does not quit the tree without having destroyed it.

299. Learn the manner of sending word to the palace.

300. Learn the manner of sitting in the presence of the King.

301. Learn the ways of the sky.

302. Learn the ways of the earth.

303. Choose a wise husband for your daughter. Do not choose for her a rich husband.

304. Do not take a wicked woman as your wife, lest she gives wicked instructions to your children.

305. If a woman whispers about her husband, they do not ever fare well.

306. If a woman does not desire the property of her husband, another man is in her heart.

307. A lowly man has no life.

308. A bad man has no wife.

309. There is a stick for sending a man out.

310. There is a stick for bringing him inside.

311. All sickness is painful. It is the wise man who knows how to be sick.

312. It is to the one who has done it that a thing happens.

313. It is to the heart that Neter looks.

314. It is in battle that a man finds for himself a brother.

315. It is on the road that a man finds for himself a companion.

316. The plans of the Ancestors are one thing and the thoughts of men are another.

317. There is one who ploughs, who does not reap.

318. There is one who reaps, who does not eat.

319. If a woman is of more exalted birth than her husband, let him give way to her.

320. The teachings of a wise man do not enter into the heart of a fool. What is in his heart, is in his heart.

321. Do not say: "I am rich in property," and so belittle the one greater than you.

322. Do not take a merchant as your friend. He lives by taking a cut.

323. Do not often speak your anger to a common man, lest you be scorned.

324. Do not be weary of calling to the Ancestors. They have their hour of listening to your needs.

GLOSSARY

Δ   Aankh Udja Seneb: Health, Prosperity and Wellness, used to greet people.

Δ   Ab: the part of our being that houses our "free will", symbolised as the heart. In African Spirituality (**AS**), we are made of nine parts, each with a specific purpose and function which can be developed and evolved into a higher level of expression.

Δ   Akhet: season of the flood in Ancient Egyptian calendar, another meaning is horizon.

Δ   Akhu: the part of our being that houses the Universal Intelligence.

Δ   Amen: hidden, inner, unseen aspect of Neter (**The All**).

Δ   Amenti: hidden land, another name for the underworld, an aspect of the mental realm.

Δ   Ammit: symbolic beast known to devour the hearts of people full of chaos and falsehood.

Δ   Anetch Hrak: salutation of power, reverence and respect.

Δ   Annu: city in Ancient Egypt.

Δ   Anpu: the force of nature that represents mediation between individuals, **The All** (Neter), and the hidden realm (Duat). Anpu is the gatekeeper, protector and guide through the hidden realm. He also serves as a teacher in his role as opener of the way (Apuat). He is normally depicted as a canine with large inquisitive ears and a sharp nose. Symbols: lavender, 3, black,

Wednesday, tobacco, coffee, carrots, canines, carnelian and doors.

Δ   Anuk: I am.

Δ   Anuk Neter: I am **The All**. A very important and symbolic truism which is the foundation and nexus of African Spirituality (**AS**).

Δ   Apep: the force of nature that represents chaos at the cosmic level, symbolised by a large serpent. It is also associated with the inability for a person to function at an optimal level, perform efficiently and achieve their goals and aspirations. Living in harmony with Maat, which is the food and drink of Ra (**The All**), allows a person to restore balance within and prosper outwards.

Δ   Apis: symbolised by the bull, the force of nature that represents fertility, strength, rebirth.

Δ   Atef: father

Δ   Atum: another name for **The All**.

Δ   Aunkh: variant of ankh, aankh and onkh which means life.

Δ   Ausar: the force of nature associated with awareness, consciousness-within, ancestry, lineage, root-cause, and the continuity of life. Ausar represents the seed of **The All** within all people. The Ausar in us, literally refers to the seat of the eye within us. In this case, he is associated with the Ba within people. The term is at times used as a sign of reverence, especially to noble Ancestors. Symbols: myrrh, 10, white, linen, crown, water and coconut.

Δ   Ausar Khenti Amenta: variant of Ausar Khenti Amentiu is a title of the oldest and wisest Sheps (Ancestor) of them all. He or She sits upon the throne among the Paut Shepsu (council of the Ancestors).

Δ   Auset: the force of nature that represents motherhood, women, healing, medicine, words of power, queenship, rivers, ritual power, trance, dreams, devotion, etc. The Holy Mother Nature. She is associated with the Ka within people. Symbols: jasmine, 7, turquoise, Monday, milk, melons and mother nursing a baby.

Δ Ba: the seat of the power and intelligence of **The All** within us (umoya). It is said to come from the father during conception of a child. It is the masculine counterpart of the Ka.

Δ Banebdjetet: an aspect of Ausar.

Δ Duamutef Sa Heru: one of Heru's four sons.

Δ Duat: the hidden world or realm.

Δ Edfu: a place in ancient Egypt (Kamit).

Δ Geb: the force of nature that represents the physical realm, earthly experience, manifestation and physical things. Geb is a male counterpart to Nut (mental realm)..

Δ Hapi: the force of nature that governs the Nile River. Places, people and things have a specific force of nature that governs them in African Spirituality (**AS**).

Δ Hapi Sa Heru: one of Heru's four sons.

Δ Heb Nen: ancient festival of surrendering.

Δ Heh: eternity.

Δ Heka: word of power. Words have power in African Spirituality (**AS**), a power that can influence people, things and events.

Δ Hekau: plural of heka.

Δ Heru: the force of nature that represents heroism, kingship, overcoming, becoming, self-awareness, freedom, and the will. Symbolised as the son of Ausar and Auset in African Spirituality (**AS**). The ultimate goal of every individual is to become a Heru (enlightened) on earth through living a life of Maat. Heru is a symbol of the fully realised and aware individual. Symbols: frankincense, 6, red, Sunday, red wine and hawk.

Δ   Heru Behudet: the force of nature that represents protection from enemies, war, justice, athleticism, competition, courage, might, relentlessness, business ventures, etc. Symbols: pine, 11, red, Tuesday, vodka, cigars, tiger's eye and hawk.

Δ   Heru Neb Taui: Heru lord of the two lands.

Δ   Heru Nej Atef: Heru avenger of his father (Ausar). Ausar is killed by Set in our sacred story, and Heru assumes this form to avenge his father.

Δ   Heru Pa Khrat: Heru the child, another form of Heru.

Δ   Herukhuti: name of the planet Mars, and is sometimes used to refer to Heru Behudet.

Δ   Het: house.

Δ   Het Heru: force of nature that represents love, joy, music, dance, young women, sexuality, fertility, and creation. She also symbolises the source of creation and is referred to as "Divine Hand of Ra." In this case, she is the physical universe that we see in all its beauty, splendour and glory. Her name means House of Heru. Symbols: rose, 5, yellow, Friday, white wine, honey, bells and diamonds.

Δ   Hetepu: offerings of peace, blessings, which is used as a salutation.

Δ   Hor-em-akhet: Heru of the horizon, real name of the so-called "sphinx."

Δ   Hotep: variant of hetepu.

Δ   Ikheru Enen: I throw myself down in surrender, I submit to you.

Δ   Imhotep, Ptah-Hotep, Kagemni, Ka-Khepera-Seneb, Dua-Khety, Merikara, Amenemope, Hordedef: eight prominent sages of Kamit (Ancient Egypt).

Δ   Imset Sa Heru: one of Heru's four sons.

- Δ Isfet: chaos, complete disorder and confusion and at times symbolises evil in African Spirituality (**AS**). Essentiality, in **AS** evil is the effect of chaos.
- Δ Ita Em: who comes as.
- Δ Ka: the part of our being that houses our personality, uniqueness. It is said to come from the mother during conception of a child. It is the feminine counterpart of the Ba.
- Δ Kamit: the original name of Ancient Egypt. It means land of black people (km.t).
- Δ Kamityu: the name of the black people of Kamit.
- Δ Kau: plural of ka.
- Δ Khaibit: the part of our being that houses our life-force (isithunzi).
- Δ Khat: the part of our being that houses our physical body (umzimba).
- Δ Khebsenuf Sa Heru: one of Heru's four sons.
- Δ Khem: black.
- Δ Khemenu: city in Ancient Egypt.
- Δ Khemmis: city in Ancient Egypt, original name is Akhmim.
- Δ Kheperu: the form that **The All** changes into in order to create.
- Δ Kheri Heb: priest.
- Δ Khert-Neter: another name for the hidden world (Duat). A vast world given many names to depict different aspects of it, depending on the story and its purpose therein.
- Δ Khmun: city in Ancient Egypt.
- Δ Khonsu: the force of nature associated with travelling, motion. He also represents time, destiny, and the Moon with its effects on the earth.
- Δ Khu: light.

Δ   Khunm: the force of nature associated with the creation of form and function, depicted as a potter. Khnum is responsible for creating the Ka (personality) and Khat (physical body) of every person. In this aspect, he also represents fertility and wealth.

Δ   Maa Kheru: true of word and deed (true of voice), it means one who speaks truth.

Δ   Maat: the force of nature that represents and embodies the laws of nature (natural laws of **The All**). She is associated with truth, reciprocity, righteousness, order, justice, balance and harmony. In order for life to exist creation takes place through Maat. All the various things, people and events in existence interact and work interdependently in a *super ecosystem* governed by Maat. In our sacred stories of African Spirituality (**AS**), it is said that before **The All** created the universe, it laid its foundation on **Maat**. That is to say, creation could not occur without first laying down the law. Symbols: honeysuckle, 2, light blue, Thursday, lapis lazuli, grapes, white feather and lady with a measuring scale.

Δ   Meht-Ur: the force of nature associated with bringing an aspect of creation into being and great floods also known as Mehet Weret.

Δ   Men Ab: stabilise the heart.

Δ   Meri: love.

Δ   Mesu: child.

Δ   Mut Neter: another name for Auset which means mother or mother nature.

Δ   Neb Metu Neter: lord of the word of **The All**.

Δ   Neb-er-Tcher: another name for **The All** which means **Lord of All**.

Δ   Nebt Het: the force of nature associated with physical beauty, body, matter, labour, service, etc. Her name means "Lady of the House." Without Nebt Het, there is no physical life, no matter, no experience.

- △ Nebt Tep Ihet: another name for Auset which means "Lady of the Cow's Head," the beheader of the rebel.
- △ Nefer: beautiful.
- △ Nehes: land south of Kamit.
- △ Nehem Neter: Saving Neter, the process of awakening the hidden Intelligence within, and enabling it to express its full wisdom and power.
- △ Neith: the force of nature associated with creation as the female expression of **The All**. She is the Great mother of all the Neteru and is considered the Supreme Being in some sacred stories.
- △ Nejem: variant of netchem, which means pleasure.
- △ Nej Kheret: how are you.
- △ Nekhebet: one of the forces of nature that represents psychic ability. The other one is Wadjet.
- △ Nesu: king.
- △ Nesut: queen.
- △ Neter: **The All**, sometimes the word is used to depict an aspect of **The All**. In African Spirituality (**AS**), there is only **One Being** in existence. We are all within this **One Being**. That is to say, all people, plants, animals and things exist within, and are part of, this **One Being**. The words, **Neter**, **One Being** and **The All** mean the same thing.
- △ Netert: female force of nature (female Neter).
- △ Netertu: female forces of nature (plural of Netert).
- △ Neteru: forces of nature (plural of Neter). In African Spirituality (**AS**), the universe is *one super-ecosystem* with *mainly* the physical realm (Geb) and mental realm (Nut). For simplicity, we will not discuss the *unformed, unmanifested or undifferentiated* state. The *super-ecosystem* is *alive* and is a unity, governed by various

forces of nature (Neteru) which permeate everything in the physical realm and mental realm. These forces of nature are a unity (Neter). But this unity (Neter) expresses itself as many forces of nature (Neteru).

Δ   Nut: force of nature that represents the mental realm, mind, and memory, symbolised by the sky. Nut is a female counterpart to Geb (physical realm).

Δ   Pa Neter: the Neter.

Δ   Paut Neteru: council of the forces of nature.

Δ   Paut Shepsu: council of the Ancestors.

Δ   Pert Em Heru: coming forth by day.

Δ   Ptah: force of nature that brought forth the universe using the power of thought and speech. It is associated with blueprints, design, architecture, structure, craftsmanship, creation, etc. It is the innate hidden intelligence that permeates all of existence.

Δ   Punt: Kingdom of Punt was South-East of Kamit. A trading partner of Kamit. It was also referred to as "Ta Neter" as in land of **The All**.

Δ   Ra: the force of nature that is responsible for bringing creation into being. **The All** assumes this form and function in order to create. The symbol of Ra is the sun. However, Ra is NOT the sun. The sun was called aten in Kamit. That is to say, Ra is NOT a sun-god. The concept of gods and goddesses is NOT part of true African Spirituality (**AS**). It is a foreign misunderstanding of Africa, African Culture and Spirituality. In African Spirituality (**AS**), the universe (all of existence) is categorised into different forces of nature (Neteru). And all these forces of nature (Neteru) constitute **One Being** (Neter). Everything ever created and in existence is part and parcel of this **One Being** (Neter). Every person, thing and event **exists inextricably** within this **One Being**, and is NOT separate from it. The **One**

Being can neither be created nor destroyed. It can only be transferred or changed from one form to another. The sacred stories of African Spirituality (**AS**), seek to chronicle systematically the change, transference and evolution, of this **One Being**.

Δ   Ra-Herukhuti: another form of **The All.**

Δ   Ren: the part of our being that houses our name. That is why it is important to give a child a good and proper name. Appropriately chosen, a child's name holds power.

Δ   Sahu: the part of our being that houses memory (ingcondo).

Δ   Sebau: forces of chaos, associated with Sebek.

Δ   Sebek: the force of nature associated with duality (good and bad), illusions, trickery, unpredictability, symbolism, fierceness, terror, animalism, exorcism, etc. His main symbol is a crocodile.

Δ   Seker-Ausar: a form of Ausar.

Δ   Sekhet: variant of Sekhmet, a warrior, raging and destructive force of nature that takes over when there is disharmony and imbalance depicted by a lioness. It is a force of correction, justice and rebalancing. Her titles are: one before whom evil trembles, mistress of the dead, lady of slaughter, she who mauls.

Δ   Sen: brother.

Δ   Senebty: may you be healthy.

Δ   Senet: sister, also refers to a board game.

Δ   Serket: female force of nature associated with protection, scorpions, and healing venomous stings and bites. Her name means "She Who Causes the Throat to Breathe". Her main symbol is a scorpion.

Δ   Set: force of nature which represents chaos, storms, jealousy, warmongering, genocide, theft of property and legacy, misappropriation, mass destruction, systematic oppression, divisiveness, forked-tongues, etc.

Δ Shekhem: the part of our being that houses the Universal Power.

Δ Shem em hotep: go in peace.

Δ Sheps: noble Ancestor (Lidlozi).

Δ Shepsu: noble Ancestors (Amadlozi), plural of Sheps.

Δ Shu: the force of nature which represents masculinity, expansion, heat, symbolised by air and space. Shu is a male counterpart to Tefnut (contraction).

Δ Ta: land.

Δ Ta-meri: beloved land, sometimes used to refer endearingly to Kamit.

Δ Ta-tenen: another form of Neter (**The All**) during creation, the name means "risen land" or "exalted earth." In African Spirituality (**AS**), creation stories are similar, but emphasise different aspects of Neter, depending on the wisdom that is being imparted in that story. That is to say, it is *one master story* being told from different angles.

Δ Tatchesert: another name for the mental realm, hidden world.

Δ Tefen, Befen, Mestet, Mestetef, Petet, Tetet and Maatet: seven scorpions that sometimes accompany Auset for protection and healing.

Δ Tefnut: the force of nature which represents femininity, contraction symbolised by water and moisture. Tefnut is a female counterpart to Shu (expansion).

Δ Tehuti: the force of nature which represents divine intelligence, wisdom, intuition, peace-making, and sages. Tehuti is associated with writing, language and high sciences. He is the Great Infinite Mind, since he knows everything. Symbols: lotus, 8, blue, Thursday, lapis lazuli, writing, scales and ibis.

Δ Tehuti Up Rehui: one of Tehuti's titles as the judge of the two fighters, brothers.

Δ Temu: another name for **The All**.

Δ Tu: yes.

Δ Tua: variant of dwa, which means thank you.

Δ Udjat: eye of Heru, symbol of awareness, attention, awakening, enlightenment, good health, empowerment, natural protection, etc.

Δ User: power.

Δ Ur: great.

Δ Ur Nebt Hekau: another title for Auset which means great lady of power.

Δ Utchat: variant of udjat.

Δ Wehem Aankh: to repeat life, which means to reincarnate.

Δ Yakhu: enlightened Ancestors.

Δ Zep Tepi: first time, first occasion.

THE GREAT TEMPLE OF QUEEN HATSHEPSUT

Behind every African lies a great foundation that
was laid down by our illustrious black Ancestors,
upon which we can rebuild eternally.

Made in the USA
Middletown, DE
23 February 2023

25477974R00217